Building Self-Esteem in Students:

A Skill and Strategy Workbook for Teachers

by

George Redman, Ph.D.

Published by Parenting & Teaching Publications, Inc., 16686 Meadowbrook Lane, Wayzata, Minnesota 55391.

Printed in the United States of America

Cover Illustration: Thielen Printing, Minneapolis, Minnesota
Editor: Kerstin Gorham
Contributing Editor: Kate Touhey
Layout & Graphics: Katherine Kenimer
Format Editing: Bill Guelscher
Content Review: Gene Anderson, Charlotte Rogers
Photography: Linda McNary

ISBN: 1-879276-01-1

Dedication

To teachers who want to help students

gain the self-esteem they need to

become all they can be.

*Teachers may already
be the most important
adult in the lives of
many children.*

— Richard Green, deceased
Chancellor, New York Public Schools

ABOUT THE AUTHOR

A former public school teacher, Dr. Redman is currently a professor of
education and on the graduate faculty of Hamline University in St. Paul,
Minnesota. The father of two children, he is a consultant and lecturer
to parent, teacher, and other professional groups on topics related to
parenting and teaching. He is director of PARENTING/TEACHING FOR
SELF-ESTEEM, a Minneapolis/St. Paul-based organization that offers
speaking and training services to teachers, parents, and others who seek
to improve the welfare of children and youth. Dr. Redman is coauthor of
Self-Esteem for Tots to Teens (1984, revised and expanded 1991), as well
as the author of numerous articles published in professional journals.
He is the recipient of a national award from the Association of Teacher
Educators for outstanding research in education.

ACKNOWLEDGMENTS

I thank the hundreds of teachers, parents, and others who work with children who participated in the presentations, workshops, and courses I have offered over the past fifteen years. Their comments and encouragement have contributed immensely to this workbook's development.

I acknowledge the many invaluable contributions of Dr. Eugene M. Anderson, who has helped develop many of the ideas presented in this workbook. His guidance and support in formulating and writing both *Self-Esteem for Tots to Teens* (1984, 1991) and this workbook are much appreciated.

For editing the manuscript I thank Kerstin Gorham and for layout and graphics, Katherine Kenimer. Both have done valiant work.

Finally, I would like to thank my wife, Shari, and my children, Angela and Ryan, for their help, patience, and moral support in my effort to translate my concerns for children into materials for teachers.

TABLE OF CONTENTS

PREFACE . . . . *xi*

INTRODUCTION 1

PART I: SKILLS FOR BUILDING SELF-ESTEEM

SKILL GROUP ONE: LISTENING TO AND ACKNOWLEDGING THOUGHTS AND FEELINGS 9
   Objective 9
   Skills:
      Paraphrasing 9
      Empathizing 10
      Asking Open Questions 11
      Asking Clarifying Questions 12
      Responding Nonverbally 15
   Concluding Statement 15
   Questions 16
   Review 17
   Your Questions 17
   Field Application 18

SKILL GROUP TWO: STRUCTURING FOR SUCCESS 19
   Objective 19
   Skills:
      Setting Appropriate Expectations 19
      Clarifying Expectations 23
      Providing Attractive Incentives 24
      Providing the Appropriate Amount of Help 25
      Removing Obstacles 27
      Setting Appropriate Standards 28
   Concluding Statement 29
   Questions 29
   Review 30
   Your Questions 31
   Field Application 31

SKILL GROUP THREE: GIVING STUDENTS FEELINGS OF REASONABLE CONTROL 33
   Objective 33
   Skills:
      Avoiding Power Struggles 34
      Avoiding Feelings of Neglect and Distrust 37
   Concluding Statement 38
   Questions 38
   Review 38
   Your Questions 39
   Field Application 40

SKILL GROUP FOUR: Reinforcing Students as Lovable and Capable 41
    Objective 41
    Skills:
        Offering Specific Encouragement and Praise 41
        Being Specific about Negative Behavior 42
        Separating the Behavior from the Person 43
        Helping Students Avoid Generalizing Negative Messages 45
        Reinforcing Effort 45
        Reinforcing Risk-Taking 46
        Reinforcing Taking Personal Responsibility 47
        Reinforcing Improvement 48
        Reinforcing Accomplishments of Which Students May Not Be Aware 48
        Reinforcing Feelings of Being Lovable 49
    Concluding Statement 50
    Questions 50
    Review 51
    Your Questions 52
    Field Application 52

SKILL GROUP FIVE: Modeling a Positive View of Yourself 55
    Objective 55
    Skills:
        Talking Positively About Yourself 55
        Communicating That You Can Admit Mistakes and Rebound from Them 56
        Taking Reasonable Risks 57
        Communicating That Helping Others Benefits One's Own Self-Esteem 57
        Converting Put-Downs to Statements of Self-Approval 58
        Modeling Persistence 59
        Identifying Traits/Interests Common to You and Your Students 59
    Concluding Statement 60
    Questions 60
    Review 61
    Your Questions 61
    Field Application 62

PART II: STRATEGIES FOR BUILDING SELF-ESTEEM

Proven Strategies for Applying the Self-Esteem Principles in the Classroom 65
Designing a Personal Action Plan 73
Conclusion 75

APPENDICES

Appendix A: Using the Principles in the Classroom
            Structuring for Success with Small Groups 79
Appendix B: Bibliography 83
Appendix C: Materials for Individuals and for
            Instructors of Workshops and Courses 89

PREFACE

This workbook is designed to help you learn, practice, and apply communication skills and teaching strategies for building self-esteem in students. It is based on the five principles outlined in the book *Self-Esteem for Tots to Teens* by Anderson, Redman, and Rogers (1984, revised and expanded 1991). You may use this workbook without other materials. However, first reading *Self-Esteem for Tots to Teens* will help you better understand the principles behind the skills.

The exercises that follow will help you expand your skills for building self-esteem through a "learning-by-doing," step-by-step process in which you

1. Become aware of the essential parts of each skill.
2. Recognize an example of the skill.
3. Perform the skill in writing and then orally in a hypothetical situation.
4. Receive constructive feedback on the adequacy of your skill performance.
5. Apply the skill in a real-life situation.
6. Receive feedback on your application of the skill in a real-life situation.

These exercises have helped both *individual* teachers, parents, and other care givers, as well as those in workshops, courses, and other *group* settings. To facilitate using the workbook in classes and staff development workshops, guidelines are provided for learning and practicing the skills in small groups.

It has been said that "If the only tool in one's toolbox is a hammer, all problems will be viewed as nails." Because the problems related to low self-esteem are diverse, our purpose is to provide you more tools for building young people's self-esteem. As you acquire new skills and polish old ones, you will become more resourceful and more confident in working with students.

Note: The skills outlined in this workbook are designed to help prevent low self-esteem and related difficulties, e.g., certain classroom misbehaviors. You may also want to improve your skills in assertiveness, problem solving, conflict resolution, and crisis intervention to help you deal with unanticipated or more severe student behavior.

DEVELOPING SKILLS

People develop skills somewhat differently than they gain knowledge. Your success in mastering skills is related to your natural abilities, your sense of purpose and commitment, your innate tendencies, and your willingness to practice.

Natural Abilities
In any field or endeavor, some people possess natural ability. Some are natural athletes, some are inherently musical, and some have a genius for writing. Even those who do not possess great ability in an area can, however, through learning and practice attain enough mastery to perform adequately. Many people with only limited athletic abilities become respectable tennis players. Others without a flair for language become competent writers. For most tasks of life, mastery does not require genius; competence does not require perfection.

Therefore, you do not have to have an innate understanding of human psychology to establish a good psychological environment for children. Through study and practice anyone can effectively foster a sense of self-worth in young people.

Sense of Purpose

People learn best when they know the purpose of what they are learning. Hence, we introduce each new skill group and each of the less familiar skills by briefly explaining its purpose.

For example, in introducing the skill of "paraphrasing" we point out that a key purpose of using the skill is to demonstrate to a student you have heard what he or she said. A second purpose might be to check your interpretation of the student's message. Following the statements of purpose for a given skill, we proceed with instructions for learning and practicing the skill.

Innate Tendencies

In developing skills, people must often overcome some innate tendencies that impede mastery. In learning golf, for example, a right-handed person must hold the left arm straight, without bending the elbow. Most of us have a decided tendency to bend both elbows, as we do when swinging a baseball bat. To drive a golf ball well, we have to overcome that tendency to bend the left elbow.

In this workbook we attempt to identify many of the natural inclinations that may impede skill mastery, and then frame the actual skill activity in terms of overcoming those inclinations.

Practice

In mastering a skill, repetition is important. To learn skills for developing student self-esteem, it is essential that you practice them. Moreover, although applying a skill feels more natural when done within a real-life context, you should first practice in a structured situation without distractions and complications. When your skills are honed, you will be able to use them with ease in real life.

THE BIG PICTURE

Building self-esteem in children is more than just a passing fancy that will disappear when the next idea comes along. Psychologists, social workers, psychiatrists, and other professionals working with children are sensitive to the relationship between self-esteem and social pathology. Often the underachiever, the drop-out, the drug user, the criminal, the potential suicide, and the "failure" exhibit deficiencies in self-esteem. Experts agree that a healthy sense of self-worth is key to a child's growth and development.

Indeed, states implementing promising new school improvement programs for the 21st century include knowledge and skills for building self-esteem as a critical part of those programs. From California to Michigan to Tennessee, states have placed self-esteem high on their list of priorities. Minnesota's outcome-based education program (OBE) includes knowledge and skills for building self-esteem as a critical desired outcome for graduation from high school. Building self-esteem is no passing fad.

Children's sense of self-esteem relates directly to their sense of *hope*. Children with low self-esteem see little hope for themselves, their society, their future. They believe that outside forces will always crush them, no matter what they do.

The adult who works to enhance a child's sense of self-esteem is saying to the child, "The world is a good place to be, and you have a place within that world." In building a child's sense of self-esteem, we teach the child that he or she has the inner strength to change the world for the better. For this child, the future holds promise.

*　　　*　　　*

INTRODUCTION

The Nature of Self-Esteem

Self-esteem is the degree to which we regard ourselves as worthy of affection and respect, that is, the degree to which we feel lovable and capable. Self-esteem stems largely from feeling loved and from feeling able to cope effectively with problems of everyday life.

Each person posesses an overall or "global" self-esteem and a sense of self-worth in a variety of areas: intellectual, physical, social, emotional, and spiritual. Our self-esteem in each of these areas is based on hundreds of thousands of successes or failures in that area.

Although self-esteem in adults is primarily determined by their own internal evaluations of their lovability and capability, self-esteem in children depends more on the external evaluations of others. Teachers, as significant others in children's lives, have an opportunity to help children feel loved and feel they can cope with academic, social, and physical challenges in schools.

Although a person's self-esteem is relatively stable and cannot be drastically altered in a short period of time, it can be changed. Furthermore, no matter how old a child, we can apply skills that will help the child improve his or her self-image. We can make a difference at any age.

Factors That Contribute to Low and High Self-Esteem

There are many contributors to low self-esteem in children (and for that matter, adults). Among the leading ones are

- Constant rejection of their thoughts and feelings.
- Repeated failure in intellectual, physical, and social endeavors.
- Domination or neglect.
- Unrelenting criticism without any reinforcement.
- Role models who demonstrate low feelings of self-worth.

The principles described in *Self-Esteem for Tots to Teens* and the skills in this workbook address these sources of low self-esteem. To build self-esteem we must

- Listen to and acknowledge the thoughts and feelings of children.
- Set children up for success.
- Give children feelings of reasonable control over their environment.
- Reinforce children as both lovable and capable.
- Model (exemplify) feelings of being lovable and capable ourselves.

Strong and Healthy vs Weak or False Self-Esteem

Some books and programs suggest that building self-esteem is simply a matter of heaping more praise on children and being more permissive when conflict arises. In fact, this approach may produce what Dr. Stephan Glenn calls "praise junkies"—children who become more dependent on others for feelings toward self, and who have a false sense of who they are and what they can do. While reinforcing children is important (see the fourth principle listed above), it cannot—even when implemented appropriately—by itself lead to a strong, realistic and generally healthy sense of self-worth.

Each of the five principles listed above contributes an important dimension to a well-balanced program for building self-esteem. Children who observe that their thoughts and feelings are taken seriously, that they often succeed at tasks they attempt, that they have some influence over their environment, that others appreciate what they do and who they are, and that others feel good about themselves, are likely to conclude that they are lovable and capable. All five principles taken together are a necessary part of a program for promoting a vital, realistic, healthy sense of self-esteem.

Further Research and Development

Since the five principles were identified in 1980, they have been examined and tried out by groups in workshops and graduate classes; and individually, by hundreds of teachers, parents, day care providers, mental health professionals and others who work with children. Each principle (as well as the group of five) has been enthusiastically endorsed as having validity, as being practical, i.e., easy to learn and use, and as being an important contributor to the self-esteem of children. In short, deliberate observations by knowledgeable persons over a period of more than 12 years support the validity and utility of the principles and skills.

While the principles and skills have met tests of conceptual analysis and the test of the use over time, empirical research would further verify their effectiveness. Such research has been designed and a pilot study completed. The pilot explored the effects of a nine-week collaborative school/college staff development program focusing on the five principles for building self-esteem in students. Paired samples t-tests on data collected using the Self-Perception Profile for Children (Harter, 1985) revealed the following statistically significant increases in levels of self-esteem in students taught by the teachers trained in the use of the principles:

	N	Grade Level	Pre-test	Post-test	t	p
Scholastic self-esteem scale	116	4-12	2.29	2.39	2.08	.02
	30	9-12	2.20	2.54	4.40	.00
Global self-esteem scale	54	4-5	2.4	2.49	2.04	.02

In the absence of a control group, the significant gains cannot be technically attributed to the program; however, it can be noted that students in the classes of the trained teachers gained significantly on the scales outlined above during the nine-week period in which the program was conducted.

Plans to replicate this study using control groups are underway at the time of this writing. One modification to be made is the expansion of the period during which the principles and skills are applied in the classroom. Because self-esteem is relatively stable, it is hypothesized that positive changes greater than those identified in the pilot study will occur if the treatment period is expanded from nine weeks to perhaps six months.

The Effects of Self-Esteem

The importance of self-esteem cannot be overestimated, for it profoundly affects many aspects of students' lives.

• **Achievement and Motivation.** Studies show that when children achieve in an academic area (e.g., math) their feelings of competence in that area increase (Connell, 1981; Harter and Connell, 1982). Furthermore, not only does their academic self-esteem in that area increase, but in children for whom academic performance is important, so does their level of motivation toward learning (Nucci, in Reynolds, ed., 1989).

While there is evidence that increased academic success in a given academic area contributes to improved academic self-esteem in that area, there seems to be less support for claims that enhancing children's general self-esteem contributes directly to greater academic success (Marsh, Smith and Barnes,1985).

• **Discipline**. Many discipline problems in schools arise from low self-esteem in students. Experts attribute many common classroom problems such as student disruption, inattention, and apathy to feelings of low self-esteem (Burns, 1979).

The key to effective discipline is preserving or enhancing self-esteem while changing unacceptable behavior. Teachers who do not maintain their students' self-esteem will tend to be less effective in managing discipline problems.

- **Teenage pregnancy**. Studies have shown that teenage girls who become pregnant tend to have lower than normal self-esteem (Patten, 1983; Held, 1981). To help children become less vulnerable to pressures that might lead to pregnancy, we need to help them in the elementary and middle-school years to develop feelings of being lovable and capable.

- **Stress, depression, and suicide**. Research (Battle, J., 1980) and professional opinion suggest that the greater one's self-esteem, the greater one's ability to resist the forces that contribute to stress, depression, and suicide. While other physiological and psychological factors can also contribute to these problems, self-esteem is often an important contributing factor and one that adults can significantly influence.

- **Addictive behaviors**. "While low self-esteem cannot be said to *cause* addictive, compulsive behavior, I have never met an addict with high self-esteem." These words come from a recovering drug addict and experienced drug counselor (Crawford, D., personal communication, 1991) at a major New York treatment center. In prevention of addiction as well as in recovery from it, building self-esteem is a vital step.

Communication and Self-Esteem

All messages imply acceptance or rejection. Evidence abounds that harsh communication as well as a lack of communication leads to low self-esteem. One study found that the level of competence a child exhibits is strongly related to the quantity and quality of communication directed to the child in his or her early years (White, et al, 1979). A study of infants housed in institutions found that a large percentage of the infants, though well fed, died from communication deprivation (Spitz, 1945).

Communicating acceptance and rejection to children over time has a powerful and direct effect on their self-esteem. If we want children to develop self-esteem, we must send messages that imply acceptance—that suggest they are lovable and capable.

Developmental Considerations In Building Self-Esteem

We can convey to students that they are lovable and capable much more easily if our communication is geared to the developmental stages at which they are operating. We can't expect children to think, feel, or behave like adults; doing so sets them up for failure.

Young children tend to be impulsive, self-centered, externally influenced, concrete in their thinking, and reward-seeking and punishment-avoiding (Anderson, et al, 1991). Consequently, when communicating with very young pupils, keep in mind the following guidelines:

- Keep comments and questions short and simple.
- Accept the expression of impulsive *desires*, without necessarily permitting impulsive *acts*.
- Accept some reward-seeking and punishment-avoiding statements.

Teaching techniques should also be geared to children's stages of development. The younger the child, the greater the need for structure and guidance. Although even young children need to explore, they need "structured exploration" that is safe and likely to be beneficial. When teaching young children

- Use concrete objects that students can hear, see, smell, taste, and/or touch.
- Present facts and concepts before encouraging discussion.
- Provide examples of what you expect.
- Display clear rules that are short and stated in positive terms.
- Provide opportunities for choice within defined limits, gradually expanding limits as students appear ready for more freedom.

You can decrease the amount of structure and guidance you give older students. When teaching older pupils

- Allow students more choice concerning the content of the course.
- Allow students more choice concerning the process of the course.
- Encourage greater creativity and higher-level thinking.
- Encourage more individual goal-setting and more self-evaluation.
- Encourage students to show more concern for others.

Keep these developmental considerations in mind as you do the exercises that follow and as you apply the self-esteem-building skills in your classroom.

Conclusion

Teachers who want to foster motivation, academic achievement, and more responsible social behavior—and who want to increase children's resistance to forces undermining those goals—need to employ skills for building self-esteem. When they do, classrooms will be more positive, productive, and pleasant for both teachers and students.

Adults who learn practical ways to foster self-esteem do a better job of building it in children. Once you learn the skills in this workbook, you will find that nurturing self-esteem is as easy as undermining it.

The knowledge that you have done your best to prepare a child for his or her entire life is both exciting and satisfying. You have an awe-inspiring opportunity to help children come to feel lovable and capable, so that on their own they will confidently, compassionately, and competently face the challenges of life.

*   *   *

Each of us is like an unfinished sunset.
Radiating our own special kind of light on things.
Beautiful yet always becoming.
Waiting to be appreciated.

— Jayne Trammel

The Organization of the Workbook

Part I of this workbook describes sets of practical skills for implementing each of the five principles of self-esteem outlined in *Self-Esteem for Tots to Teens*. We call these sets of skills "skill groups." For each skill in a given skill group, we provide a simple definition of the skill, at least one example of how to use it correctly, a brief written exercise, and a role-playing activity for practicing the skill in small groups.

Each skill group also contains a set of questions to stimulate further thought, a review section to help reinforce learning, and a "Field Application" section that provides guidelines for applying selected skills in your classroom or school.

Part II focuses on proven strategies for building self-esteem in the classroom and on designing a personal action plan for further study.

Appendix A provides a more detailed example of how one of the five principles can help teachers use small groups more effectively. Appendix B contains an extensive bibliography for educators. Appendix C describes other resources for building self-esteem available to teachers and teacher educators.

Building a Temple

A builder built a temple,
He wrought it with grace and skill;
Pillars and groins and arches,
All fashioned to work his will.
Men said, as they saw its beauty,
"It shall never know decay.
Great is thy skill, O builder;
Thy frame shall endure for aye."

A teacher built a temple
With loving and infinite care,
Planning each arch with patience,
Laying each stone with prayer.
None praised her unceasing efforts;
None knew of her wondrous plan.
For the temple the teacher built
Was unseen by the eyes of man.

Gone is the builder's temple
Crumbled into the dust;
Low lies each stately pillar,
Food for consuming rust.
But the temple the teacher built
Will last while the ages roll,
For that beautiful unseen temple
Is a child's immortal soul.

— Author Unknown

Part I:

Skills for

Building Self-Esteem

TEACHERS AFFECT ETERNITY.

— Henry James

SKILL GROUP ONE:
LISTENING TO AND ACKNOWLEDGING THOUGHTS AND FEELINGS

"No one ever listens to me" is a response we hear often from children. They have learned that the tendency of many adults is to speak rather than listen to children's needs and interests.

The purpose of skill group one is to help you review several skills for demonstrating to pupils that you *have* listened to them and that you understand what they have said. By employing such skills, you communicate to students that they are worthy of being heard, hence that they are worthy of esteem.

Objective: To know and be able to apply effective listening skills.

SKILL: PARAPHRASING

The purpose of paraphrasing is to show that you have heard what another person has said. It also allows you to see if your perception of what was said is correct. To paraphrase a thought or feeling is to restate it in slightly different words without losing the original meaning. For example, if a student was to say, "I can't get this problem," you might paraphrase by saying, "You're having some trouble with number 10, huh?"

Other ways of beginning paraphrasing statements include:

- So you're saying that . . .
- OK, so you think that . . .
- Let me tell you what I am hearing: you feel . . .

* In the space provided, write a statement involving some thought or feeling that a student has communicated to you.

_____

_____

* Now write a paraphrase (restatement) of that thought or feeling.

_____

_____

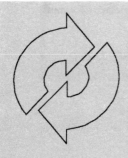

If you are in a group learning situation, form a group of three persons. Designate a "sender," a "receiver," and an "observer." Have the sender read the thought or feeling that he/she has just written. Have the receiver paraphrase the thought or feeling. Have the observer provide constructive feedback on the effectiveness of the paraphrase. Have the sender also provide feedback.

Rotate roles so that each person in your group has the opportunity to be sender, receiver, and observer. *

List any suggestions for improvement.

1.

2.

SKILL: EMPATHIZING

Empathizing is the process of communicating understanding of another's thought or feeling. In empathizing, you needn't share the thought or feeling fully but must indicate that you comprehend it. Whereas the purpose of paraphrasing is to tell the other person, "I heard you," making a statement of empathy says, "I think I know how you feel." Paraphrasing and empathizing together communicate, "You are worthy of being heard and understood."

To make an empathy statement to a student who says, "Those guys don't want me in their learning group," you might respond, "It doesn't feel good when you're not included, does it?"

---

* If you are <u>not</u> in a group setting, elicit responses about what you have written from a family member, friend or colleague. If you do this for each skill in this skill group, you will gain additional insights about using each skill.

Other ways of beginning an empathy statement include:

- I think I know generally how you feel . . .
- I can imagine what you're thinking (or feeling); I've had a similar experience, and it made me feel that way, too.
- Though I can't condone the action you took, I see why you might have *felt* like doing what you did.

Note: Messages sent by young people often contain both thoughts and feelings. Adults have a tendency to reply to the thoughts rather than to the feelings. We need to recognize that when a student says, "Those guys don't want me in their group" he is undoubtedly expressing a feeling as well as a thought, even though the feeling may be somewhat hidden.

* Write a thought or feeling that a student has expressed to you.

_____

_____

* Now write an empathy statement in response to the above thought or feeling.

_____

_____

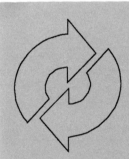

If you are in a group learning situation, form a group of three persons. Designate a "sender," a "receiver," and an "observer." Have the sender verbalize the thought or feeling that he/she wrote. Have the receiver respond with a statement of empathy. Have the observer provide constructive feedback on the effectiveness of the empathy statement. Have the sender also provide feedback.

Rotate roles so that each person in your group has the opportunity to be sender, receiver, and observer.

List any suggestions for improvement.

1.

2.

SKILL: ASKING OPEN QUESTIONS

Many adults have a tendency to ask questions that have only one "correct" answer. Such questions are called "closed" questions. Examples of closed questions include "yes or no" questions, like "Do you understand that you must return immediately to the classroom after getting a book from the library?" and questions with a single answer, like "What is two plus two?"

An "open" question is one for which there is more than one answer. For example, "What do you know about the culture of the Dakota Indians?" and "What is your understanding of our agreement regarding what you will do after getting a book from the library?" are open questions.

The purpose of open questions is to tell students that we are interested in their ideas, opinions, attitudes, and beliefs, and hence that *they* are worthy of our interest. When we ask "open" questions, we ask children to add their thinking to our thinking. By doing so we treat child thinking as complementary to adult thinking, and hence reward children as capable of contributing valuable thoughts and feelings.

* Using the context of your classroom, write a closed question.

_____

_____

* Now convert that question to a more open form.

_____

_____

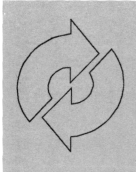

If you are in a group learning situation, in small groups have each person share his or her written question—first the closed form, then the open form. Provide constructive feedback to each other as to whether the open form effectively invites the other's point of view.

List any suggestions for improvement.

1.

2.

SKILL: ASKING CLARIFYING QUESTIONS

Children do not always send clear messages. Many adults have a tendency to respond before they are certain of the meaning of the message. A clarifying question asks the child to define a term or phrase or idea. Using clarifying questions communicates to the student that you feel it is important to understand his or her thought or feeling.

TYPES OF CLARIFYING QUESTIONS

Clarifying questions may seek either clarity of a student's *meaning* or of a student's *preference*.

Meaning. Asking for clarification of *meaning* shows that you are interested in understanding better a student's thought or feeling. For example, you might clarify a thought by asking, "What do you mean when you say that Abraham Lincoln was a neat guy?" or "When you say that this assignment is hard, which parts of it are giving you trouble?" You might clarify a feeling by inquiring, "When you say that you hate school, do you feel angry? frustrated?" or "When you say you feel lousy, what do you mean by lousy?"

The following are examples of questions designed to clarify the meaning of a thought or feeling:

- I don't understand what you mean. Would you give me an example?
- What do you mean by _____(word or phrase)?
- Can you draw a map (sketch) of where I'm to meet you?
- I hear what you are saying, but you *appear* to be feeling otherwise.

* Write a statement a student might make that reflects an unclear thought.

_____

_____

* Formulate a question you could ask to clarify the meaning of that thought.

_____

_____

* Write a statement a student might make that reflects an unclear feeling.

_____

_____

* Now write a question you could ask to clarify the meaning of that feeling statement.

_____

_____

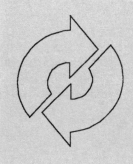

If you are in a group learning situation, form a group of three persons. Designate a "sender," a "receiver," and an "observer." Have the sender share one of his/her unclear statements regarding a thought or feeling. Have the receiver ask for clarification of meaning. Have the observer provide constructive feedback on the effectiveness of the clarifying question. Have the sender also provide feedback.

Rotate roles so that each person in your group has the opportunity to be sender, receiver, and observer.

List any suggestions for improvement.

1.

2.

Preference. Seeking clarification of *preference* also communicates that you want to understand a student's point of view. For example, you could say to a student who "sort of" wants to go to the science museum for the class field trip, "On a ten-point scale with ten being high, how badly do you want to go to the science museum?" You could ask the pupil who says she does not care whether her committee is responsible for party decorations or for entertainment, "Which responsibility would you choose if you were going to do the work by yourself?"

The following are examples of questions designed to clarify preferences:

- How strongly do you feel about this?
- What, more specifically, do you like/dislike about that?
- Would you choose that option if the consequences were . . . ?

* Write a statement a student might make that reflects an unclear preference.

_____

_____

* Now write a question that would help clarify that preference.

_____

_____

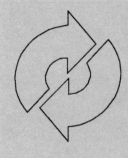
If you are in a group learning situation, form a group of three persons. Designate a "sender," a "receiver," and an "observer." Have the sender share his/her unclear statements regarding a preference. Have the receiver ask for clarification of preference. Have the observer provide constructive feedback on the effectiveness of the clarifying question. Have the sender also provide feedback.

Rotate roles so that each person in your group has the opportunity to be sender, receiver, and observer.

List any suggestions for improvement.

1.

2.

SKILL: RESPONDING NONVERBALLY

Many adults have a tendency to overlook the importance of nonverbal communication. Nonverbal responses are every bit as important as verbal responses in convincing children you are listening. The following are examples of nonverbal responses:

- **Eye contact** Maintain a comfortable level of eye contact with a child who is communicating with you. Keep in mind cultural variations in this practice. Some Asian cultures, for example, teach their young that it is a sign of respect not to look into the eyes of an adult.

- **Head nod** Nodding to acknowledge that you have heard can help show a child you are following ideas. However, children may not be convinced they were heard with a head nod only. Paraphrasing can be a useful complement.

- **Appropriate touch** Patting a child on the back, squeezing a hand, or giving a hug can show involvement in a conversation. What is an appropriate level of touch for one child may be too much for another. Ask the child if in doubt.

Smiles, gestures, and other nonverbal responses are described more fully in other books and journals. We encourage you to learn more nonverbal communication skills.

CONCLUDING STATEMENT

Successful mastery of the skills described in this skill group entails sensitizing yourself to the quality of a child's messages as well as the quality of possible adult responses. Everybody likes to feel that someone cares about what he or she has to say. The skills in this group will help show young people you feel they are important. When they believe that you feel they are lovable and capable, *they* are more likely to conclude that they are lovable and capable.

QUESTIONS

Write your answers to the following questions on a separate piece of paper. Please indicate the grade level at which you teach.

Grade Level _____

1. Which of the skills for listening and acknowledging do you use most regularly?
2. Which do you use least regularly?
3. Which of the skills are easiest for you to use? Why?
4. Which are hardest to use? Why?
5. Generally speaking, in what kinds of situations would you tend to use each of the following skills? Why?
    • paraphrasing
    • empathizing
    • asking open questions
    • clarifying meaning
    • clarifying preference
    • responding nonverbally
6. Which of the skills (if any) are more appropriate for use with students at the following levels?
    •elementary school age:
    •middle school age:
    •high school age:
   Why?
7. How would you adapt a certain skill to a particular grade level?
8. Which of the skills do you wish others would use more when interacting with you? Why?
9. How could you get others to use these skills more?
10. How could you teach your students to use the skills with each other? with adults?
11. Are there other skills related to listening and acknowledging that are important? If so, what are they?
12. If you are in a group learning situation, select one of the above questions and share your response with your group members. Note reactions that might be helpful to you in future teaching.

REVIEW

Paraphrases

> (Statement) "My mom and dad really push hard!"
> (Paraphrase) "Your parents have high expectations, huh?"

> (Statement) "This problem is too hard. I can't get it."
> (Paraphrase) "This one's giving you some trouble, huh?"

Empathy Statements

> (Statement) "My mom and dad really push hard!"
> (Empathy Statement) "It's hard sometimes to live up to adult expectations, isn't it?"

> (Statement) "This problem is too hard. I can't get it."
> (Empathy Statement) "It's frustrating, huh? Let's look at it together."

Open Questions

> (Closed) "Which of your parents pushes you harder?"
> (Open) "How does it make you feel when others expect so much?"

> (Closed) "Have you tried hard to solve that problem?"
> (Open) "What steps have you tried to solve that problem?"

Clarifying Questions

- Meaning   (Unclear) "My mom and dad push too hard!"
(Clarifying) "Can you give me an example?" or "What do they do when they push too hard?"

                  (Unclear) "This problem is too hard. I can't get it."
(Clarifying) "What parts do you understand?" (pause) "Now, what parts don't you get?"

- Preference   (Unclear) "My mom and dad push too hard!"
(Clarifying) "How strongly do you feel about it--strongly enough to talk to them about it?"

                  (Unclear) "This problem is too hard. I can't get it."
(Clarifying) "Do you want to keep at it or try a simpler one first?"

Nonverbal Response

Eye contact, head nods, appropriate touch.

YOUR QUESTIONS

1. List at least two questions you have regarding the use of the listening and acknowledging skills.
2. If you are in a group learning situation, share at least one of these questions with the members of your group. Invite responses that might be helpful to you in future teaching.

FIELD APPLICATION

Plan, implement, and evaluate a method for investigating the effectiveness of one of the listening and acknowledging skills with one or more of your students. The following is an example:

Let's say I decide to use empathy statements with Will and Sarah, two somewhat-withdrawn third graders. I plan to empathize with feelings they express at least once a day for two weeks. I will record my statements and their responses on a chart. I place a reminder to use the skill, a sign that reads "Make empathy statements" on my desk, where I will look at it often. I review my plan with colleagues.

Then I implement the plan. I record my empathy statements and each student's responses (e.g., Sarah's willingness to talk more after class, Will's increased willingness to try new things in class and to say "I can do this," or other positive behaviors that might indicate an increase in self-esteem).

When the two weeks are up, I review each student's responses and identify any patterns (e.g., that Will regularly became more communicative after an empathy statement, or that Sarah began asserting herself with other students more). I draw conclusions from my findings (e.g., that empathy statements seem to increase students' confidence in expressing themselves).

Finally, I share my findings, conclusions, and recommendations with teachers, parents, and other appropriate persons. In doing so, I protect the anonymity of my students.

The following outline is provided as a guide for planning, implementing, and evaluating an action plan for applying skills related to good listening and acknowledging:

I. **Plan** your investigation by answering the following questions:
   1. What skill from this section will you investigate?
   2. Which students will participate in your study?
   3. How and when will you use the skill?
   4. How will you remind yourself to practice the skill frequently?
   5. How will you monitor your use of the skill?
   6. What method will you use to record changes in your students' behavior that seem to result from your application of the skill?
   7. How long will your investigation last?
   8. Discuss your plan with one or two colleagues. What suggestions did they provide for improving your study?

II. **Implement** your field application plan. Record each time you use the skill and each student response to its use.

III. **Evaluate** your study:

   1. Analyze your data and identify any patterns.
   2. List the major findings and conclusions of your study.
   3. List for other teachers at your grade level recommendations for using the skill.
   4. Share what you've learned with others.

Now, if necessary, modify your approach and replicate your study. Then repeat the study using other skills for listening to and acknowledging your students.

*   *   *

SKILL GROUP TWO:
STRUCTURING FOR SUCCESS

Students cannot avoid experiencing some failures. Nor should they, for experiencing failure helps them develop a realistic view of life and teaches them important lessons. However, repeated failures can convince them they do not measure up to the standards of society, that they are by nature "failures." Students who feel this way about themselves become so cautious they will refuse almost any challenge, even those that must be met for their own well-being.

We need to set students up for success rather than failure. Structuring for success includes presenting tasks in ways that are least threatening, encouraging moderate risk taking, and convincing them that even "failing" is not so terrible, provided they have made an honest effort.

The purpose of this skill group is to help you develop skills useful in creating situations likely to lead to success for students. These exercises contain examples of what you can do to promote success.

Objective: To know and be able to apply skills for setting children up to succeed.

SKILL: SETTING APPROPRIATE EXPECTATIONS

While some expectations can be established for an entire class, those that are individually tailored enhance chances of success. Some children need more practice than others. Some need different types of explanations than do others. Some children learn more visually than verbally or symbolically. For example, when teaching "3+3," children who think more concretely would benefit by seeing three objects placed by three other objects to make six objects. Individually oriented learning activities have been shown to foster perceptions of capability (Schunk, 1985).

To ensure that pupils have a good chance of succeeding, we need to elicit from them their individual needs and interests, as well as their level of knowledge and skills, and consider those things when negotiating goals.

Eliciting needs and interests. Posing questions about children's *needs and interests* can help you determine what students are ready and eager to do. To elicit a need, you might ask, "What do you need to know in order to write this essay?" To elicit an interest, you might say, "You seem interested in learning about gangs—what makes them attractive to certain kids, what are the various roles of members and the like. Would you like to do your research project on gang behavior?"

* **Write a question that elicits a need or interest from a student.**

_____

_____

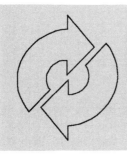

If you are in a group learning situation, in small groups have each person share his or her written question. Provide constructive feedback to each other on the effectiveness of each question. * List any suggestions for improvement.

1.

2.

Eliciting knowledge and skills. Asking questions regarding the *knowledge and skills* of students can help you establish attainable goals for your students. To discover a student's prior knowledge, you might ask, "What's your understanding of the term 'thesis statement'?" or "How could you break that goal into shorter-term and more specific objectives?" To ascertain a student's skill level, you might suggest, "Show me how you'd work through this problem."

* **Write a question that would help you determine the knowledge or skills possessed by a student.**

_____

_____

If you are in a group learning situation, in small groups have each person share his or her written question. Provide constructive feedback to each other on the effectiveness of each question. List any suggestions for improvement.

1.

2.

_____

* If you are <u>not</u> in a group setting, elicit responses about what you have written from a family member, friend or colleague. If you do this for each skill in this skill group, you will gain additional insights about using each skill.

Identifying methods or procedures needed to accomplish goals. You can help students think about the steps in solving a problem by asking questions like "What do you need to know before you can complete this step?" or "How can you get the data you need—a library search, survey of students, interviews of experts, or a combination of some of these?"

* **Write a question that would help identify a method or procedure that would help a student attain a goal.**

_____

_____

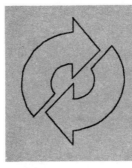

If you are in a group learning situation, in small groups have each person share his or her written question. Provide constructive feedback to each other on the effectiveness of each question. List any suggestions for improvement.

1.

2.

Research shows that student participation in goal-setting fosters feelings of self-efficacy (Schunk, 1985). Moreover, such participation fosters a sense of ownership of a task's outcome. We need to include students in the process of goal-setting whenever possible.

We can involve students in goal-setting by asking them to complete the following kinds of statements:

General goal: As a result of this project, assignment, or task, I want to be able to

_____

(know and/or appreciate something, do something, etc.)

Specifically, I would like to know

a._____

b._____

c._____

Specifically, I would like to be able to perform the skill(s) of

a._____

b._____

c._____

Specifically, I would like to be able to better appreciate

a._____

b._____

c._____

The following is an example of establishing a general goal and then breaking it down into specific parts:

General goal: As a result of this project, I want to be able to
_____*better understand the nature, causes, and effects of racism.*_____

Specifically, I would like to know

a. _____*accepted definitions of "racism."*_____

b. _____*the degree to which insecurities from childhood affect one's attitudes toward people of another racial, ethnic, or cultural background.*_____

Specifically, I would like to be able to

a. _____*communicate respect more effectively with those who are from racial, ethnic, and cultural backgrounds different from my own.*_____

Specifically, I would like to better appreciate

a. _____*customs, social norms, religious beliefs, music, and legends of persons of cultures different from my own.*_____

SKILL GROUP TWO: STRUCTURING FOR SUCCESS

* Write a brief outline of a simple plan to involve a student in setting short-term (individual) goals for a lesson or unit.

_____

_____

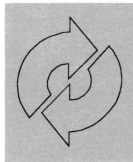

If you are in a group learning situation, in small groups have each person share his or her written outline. Provide constructive feedback to each other on the effectiveness of the outline. List any suggestions for improvement.

1.

2.

SKILL: CLARIFYING EXPECTATIONS

Teachers can also help structure their students' learning environment for success by making sure that both their own expectations (goals or objectives) and their pupils' expectations are clearly worded and understood.

Teacher expectations. We sometimes make _teacher expectations_ unclear to students by being too vague, for example, by saying, "Be back soon" or "Be nice" or "Act your age." We need to provide specific information on the who, what, where, when, why, and how of a task if we are to help children succeed. For example, you can be more specific by saying, "Be back in five minutes" or "Set your instruments down carefully to the right of your chair, [pause] stand, [pause] and, walking slowly, line up single-file at the door" or "Write a plan for your project that follows the format we outlined and discussed yesterday in class; your project plan will be due at the beginning of class Tuesday, March 24."

* Write a statement of teacher expectations that is incomplete and unclear.

_____

_____

* Now convert that statement to one that is complete and specific.

_____

_____

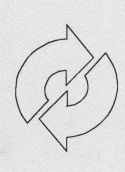

If you are in a group learning situation, form a group of three persons. Designate a "sender," a "receiver," and "observer." Have the sender share his or her incomplete or unclear statement regarding teacher expectations, and the receiver make that statement complete and specific. Have the observer provide feedback on the effectiveness of the complete and specific statement. Have the sender also provide feedback.

Rotate roles so that each person in your group has the opportunity to be sender, receiver and observer.

List any suggestions for improvement.

1.

2.

Student expectations. Teachers also need to seek clarification of *student expectations*. We can do that by asking pupils to tell us, for example, their understanding of a particular classroom rule or assignment. You might clarify student expectations by asking questions such as "What is our rule about having food in the classroom? What happens when a student breaks one of our basic rules?" or "What is your plan for carrying out your project?"

* Write a question that seeks clarification of student expectations.

_____

_____

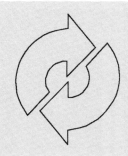

If you are in a group learning situation, in small groups have each person share his or her written question. Provide constructive feedback to each other on the effectiveness of each question. List any suggestions for improvement.

1.

2.

SKILL: PROVIDING ATTRACTIVE INCENTIVES

Since some children are naturally motivated by a "What's in it for me?" attitude, providing attractive incentives can help lead to successful achievement of educational or behavioral outcomes.

We must remember, however, that incentives attractive to adults are not always attractive to children. For example, reading teachers have reported the failure of students to read until they were allowed to read material that appealed to them—such as that in motorcycle magazines.

Observing and questioning students is essential in determining which incentives appeal to them. To get at that information, you might ask openly, "What kinds of games do you like to play in the classroom when we hold recess indoors?" or "Let's think of a reward for ourselves. If we can finish this chapter by Friday, we'll use the last fifteen minutes of the period to do something fun. What would you consider fun?"

* Write a question that would identify incentives to motivate a student to succeed.

_____

_____

If you are in a group learning situation, in small groups have each person share his or her written question. Provide constructive feedback to each other on the effectiveness of each question. List any suggestions for improvement.

1.

2.

SKILL: PROVIDING THE APPROPRIATE AMOUNT OF HELP

You can greatly enhance success in learning by providing the appropriate amount of help as students undertake tasks. The amount of help offered is important. If a teacher helps students too much, they may feel the instructor has no confidence in them. If the teacher helps too little, students may feel the teacher does not care how they do.

Determining the appropriate amount of help. We can determine the proper amount of help pupils need by looking for signs of student frustration and boredom, as well as by asking directly, "Would you like some help with this assignment?" (Avoid phrasing the question, "Do you _need_ help?" A student who answers "yes" to this question admits incompetence.)

* Write a question designed to determine the amount of help desired by a student.

_____

_____

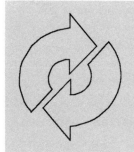
If you are in a group learning situation, in small groups have each person share his or her written question. Provide constructive feedback to each other on the effectiveness of each question. List any suggestions for improvement.

1.

2.

Strategies for providing help. Once you have determined the appropriate *amount* of help, you must provide *sources* of help. Certainly the teacher is a source, but is often already overcommitted. Structured curriculum materials, such as activity guides and workbooks or worksheets, can help. Volunteers—parents, college students, or students in your school—can also assist.

Students can also help themselves. Research shows that both self-monitoring of learning (Schunk, 1982) and self-verbalization of learning (Schunk, 1986b) can help students learn.

To *self-monitor* their learning, students keep simple records of work done. The record may take the form of a list of pages read, problems worked, grammar rules learned, and the like. Or it may resemble a journal with narrative or a series of lists, or consist of a chart with check marks. Whatever the form, self-monitoring forces students to recognize progress and hence rewards them for steps taken. The following is a simple example of a chart for self-monitoring:

DAILY LOG FOR _____ (Date)

Class _____   Hour _____

| | Problems Done | Problems I |
Problems To Do	Correctly	Need to Work On

To *self-verbalize* their learning, students state what they are doing currently and what they will do next, for example, "I'm putting the nut on the bolt and turning it to the right" or "I'm prewriting now to get creative ideas, next I'll rewrite, then I'll edit for grammar and usage, and finally I'll proofread for typos."

By learning to verbalize and to monitor their own progress, students develop self-help skills. Students can self-monitor and self-verbalize alone, with a partner, in a small group, or even at the board to the entire class.

* Write a directive to students that would encourage (or require) them to engage in self-monitoring or self-verbalization on a specific assignment.

_____

_____

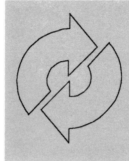

If you are in a group learning situation, in small groups have each person share his or her written directive. Provide constructive feedback to each other on the effectiveness of each directive. List any suggestions for improvement.

1.

2.

SKILL: REMOVING OBSTACLES

Sometimes obstacles prevent students from succeeding in school. Obstacles come in many forms: lack of knowledge or skills, poor study habits, negative attitudes, or distracting objects and events. Perhaps the most common (and easiest to remove) are those that have to do with the physical environment, such as inoperable tools, breakable equipment, or distracting activities within the classroom.

Some obstacles to learning and to behaving appropriately relate to inappropriate expectations. For example, setting long-term goals rather than short-term goals can impede students' progress. Likewise, asking thirty second graders to stand in close proximity while rehearsing for a concert provides the opportunity for some pushing and shoving.

Other obstacles are unique to a given student, that is, determined by the particular personality of a child. For instance, some children require absolute silence for learning, while others require a bit of background noise. Some students are easily drawn into inappropriate conversation by a classmate. By identifying particular obstacles for individual students, you can structure the environment in order to give them the maximum opportunity for success.

We should observe and question children to determine their particular obstacles to learning and behaving appropriately. To identify those obstacles, you might ask _closed questions_ such as "Is the noise from that small group disturbing your concentration?" or _open questions_ such as "What can we do to keep you from talking to John during class discussions?"

* Write an open question that would elicit from a student obstacles to his or her learning.

_____

_____

* **Write a closed question that would elicit from a student obstacles to his or her learning.**

_____

_____

* **Write an open question that would elicit from a student obstacles to his or her behaving appropriately.**

_____

_____

* **Write a closed question that would elicit from a student obstacles to his or her behaving appropriately.**

_____

_____

If you are in a group learning situation, in small groups have each person share his or her written questions. Provide constructive feedback to each other on the effectiveness of each question. List any suggestions for improvement.

1.

2.

SKILL: SETTING APPROPRIATE STANDARDS

Teachers must set appropriate standards if they expect students to succeed. Standards that are too low suggest that the teacher lacks confidence in a pupil's capability; those that are too high frustrate students. Both invite failure.

Some teachers only set standards based on perfection. By setting instead some standards that fall between minimal and optimal performance, teachers can give students credit for improvement. Rewarding improvement encourages students to do even better.

Successful strategies for determining appropriate standards include basing standards on an individual's own past performance rather than on comparisons with other students, using criterion-referenced standards (letting students meet specified criteria through different means), using mastery learning (letting students redo tasks), and specifying student outcomes desired.

* **List two specific strategies for setting appropriate standards that you have used successfully in your classes.**

_____

_____

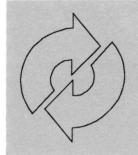

If you are in a group learning situation, in small groups have each person share his or her written strategies. Provide constructive feedback to each other on the effectiveness of each strategy. List any suggestions for improvement.

1.

2.

Holding students accountable for meeting established standards is important for building self-esteem, for it is only when students see true accomplishment that they feel more capable. Conversely, passing a student who has failed to meet a criterion does not build self-esteem, but rather, undermines it. Students passed on permissively know that they are not more capable than before. Such a process tends to produce students who graduate, but who can't read, or write, or compute. These students are not likely to feel lovable or capable academically even if (falsely) reinforced for their academic talents.

Students who fail to perform at the level specified in a given criterion must be told specifically what they did correctly and specifically what must be done in addition to meet the criterion. Then, when actual improvement is observed, the student will truly feel more capable.

In short, accountability in holding to appropriate standards contributes to self-esteem, permissiveness does not. Helping to build a healthy, robust sense of self-worth means more than simply praising students more and giving them more "breaks;" it includes helping them see their true accomplishments.

CONCLUDING STATEMENT

Children learn they are lovable and capable through experiencing success. When they see that they have been successful academically, socially, emotionally or athletically, they see themselves as more lovable and capable.

QUESTIONS

Write your answers to the following questions on a separate sheet of paper. Please indicate the grade level at which you teach.

Grade Level _____

1. Which of the skills and strategies for structuring for success were easiest for you to use? Why?
2. Which were hardest to use? Why?
3. Which skills and strategies in this section are most overlooked by teachers?
4. Which have worked best for you?
5. What skills or strategies for structuring for success not discussed here have worked well for you?
6. What have you seen other teachers do that encourages success? failure?
7. What skills and strategies for structuring for success do/could you teach your students to help them build their own self-esteem or that of their classmates?
8. If you are in a group learning situation, select one of the above questions and share your response with your group members. Note reactions that might be helpful to you in future teaching.

REVIEW

Setting Appropriate Expectations

- Eliciting needs and interests

    "What is it that you would like to accomplish in your project?"

    "What do you want to know or understand when you're done with your study?"

- Eliciting knowledge and skills

    "Can you add and subtract?"

    "How much of this kind of thing have you done before?"

- Identifying methods or procedures needed to accomplish goals

    "What do we [you] need to do first?"

    "What steps will be required to complete this task?"

Clarifying Expectations

- Stating clear expectations

    Assignment: Write a 2- to 4-page, double-spaced, typed paper on a famous scientist who is a member of a minority group. Include important influences on his or her early life, middle years, and later life. List several important accomplishments and contributions this person made to science. You may work individually or in groups of up to three persons. Due date: beginning of class, October 24.

    (For an energetic class that needs structure) "Row 1, quietly, with your hands to yourself, please line up starting at the door and continuing along this wall. . . . OK, good job; now row 2. . . . Very well done; next row 3. . . . Good."

- Clarifying student expectations

    "What do you mean when you say that you want your classmates to 'participate' in the small group discussion?"

Providing Attractive Incentives

    "If we all finish our spelling assignment by 10:00, we'll take ten minutes and do something fun. What fun thing would you like to do?"

    "If we are all done when the timer goes off, we'll be able to see the video tape on animal behavior that you wanted to see."

Providing the Appropriate Amount of Help

    "Would you like help with this next step?"

    "What kind of help do you want?"

Removing Obstacles to Success

- Obstacles to learning

   "Is the sunlight bothering your eyes?" [Privately] "Molly, it looks like you're having trouble seeing the board. Would you like to move closer to the front of the room?"

- Obstacles to behaving appropriately

   "Let's spread out farther so that when our arms are extended we won't touch one another."

Setting Appropriate Standards

   "This is a different form of the test you took three weeks ago. Let's see if you can improve your score, OK?" [Comparison based on past performance rather than on performance of other students.]

YOUR QUESTIONS

   1. List at least two questions you have regarding the use of skills for structuring for success.

   2. If you are in a group learning situation, share at least one of these questions with the members of your small group. Note their responses and any insights gained.

FIELD APPLICATION

Plan, implement, and evaluate a method for investigating the effectiveness of one of the structuring for success skills with one or more of your students. The following is an example:

Let's say I want to become more proficient at providing attractive incentives to my tenth graders, and I suspect that an incentive could motivate Keisha, Terry, and Ahmad to work harder. I decide to offer the incentive in each student's individual weekly contract: each student will be able to earn five extra credit points * by completing an assignment by a specific date. I will offer the incentives for two months and record in a notebook the weeks in which each student opts for extra credit. I review my plan with colleagues.

Once I make final modifications, I implement the plan. I record each time Keisha, Terry, or Ahmad opt for extra credit (e.g., the first week all three students opted for extra credit, the second week only Terry and Ahmad opted for it, beginning with the sixth week only Ahmad opted for it).

When the two months are up, I review student responses and identify any patterns (e.g., that extra credit seems to be effective in motivating Ahmad, initially useful in helping Terry, and ineffective in stimulating Keisha). I draw conclusions from my findings (e.g., that a given incentive or incentive schedule works best with certain types of students or in a certain time frame).

I share my findings, conclusions, and recommendations with teachers, parents, and other appropriate persons. In doing so, I protect the anonymity of my students.

_____

* For elementary students, the incentive might be stars on a chart.

The following outline is provided as a guide for planning, implementing, and evaluating an action plan for applying skills related to structuring for success.

I. **Plan** your investigation by answering the following questions.

1. What skill or strategy from this section will you investigate?
2. Which students will participate in your study?
3. How and when will you use the skill?
4. How will you remind yourself to practice the skill frequently?
5. How will you monitor your use of the skill?
6. What method will you use to record changes in your students' behavior that seem to result from your application of the skill?
7. How long will your investigation last?
8. Discuss your plan with one or two colleagues. What suggestions did they provide for improving your study?

II. **Implement** your field application plan. Record each time you use the skill and each student response to its use.

III. **Evaluate** your study.

1. Analyze your data and identify any patterns.
2. List the major findings and conclusions of your study.
3. List for other teachers at your grade level recommendations for using the skill.
4. Share what you've learned with others.

Now, if necessary, modify your approach and replicate your study. Then repeat the study using other skills for structuring for success with your students.

*   *   *

SKILL GROUP THREE:
GIVING STUDENTS FEELINGS OF REASONABLE CONTROL

Children who experience too much adult control over their lives tend to feel that no one trusts them—that adults believe they are incapable of controlling themselves. Children who experience little or no adult control over their lives often feel neglected—that no one cares about them. In either case, self-esteem suffers.

Some teachers have a tendency to not clarify for students which powers belong exclusively to teachers, which belong to students, and which are negotiable. As suggested in the previous section on structuring for success, lack of clarity can set young people up for failure. For example, some teachers often say "Maybe" to children's requests. For children, "Maybe" might mean "Yes." To avoid confusion, teachers should instead either (1) positively state some actual conditions that must be fulfilled by the child for the request to be met, or (2) state in positive terms what alternative(s) are possible, or (3) say "No" so that no confusion exists. Of the three options, the first two are far preferable. Options can be combined, e.g., "You can't sharpen your pencil now, but you can borrow one from me."

As children demonstrate a greater sense of competency and responsibility, we can make non-negotiable powers negotiable. If adults set out the non-negotiables clearly in the beginning, children will see their transformation into negotiables as expressions of confidence in them.

The purpose of the following skills is to give students a feeling of reasonable control, thereby enhancing their decision-making skills, sense of responsibility, and self-esteem. Children will not feel lovable and capable without the sense of accomplishment that comes from being able to influence aspects of their lives.

> **Objective: To know and be able to apply skills
> for giving children feelings of reasonable control.**

SKILL: AVOIDING POWER STRUGGLES

Power struggles between teachers and students are battles for control. Since such struggles tend to reduce student self-esteem (as well as disrupt class), teachers need to know strategies such as the following for reducing and avoiding them.

Offering "tradeoffs" can be profitable for both teacher and students. A tradeoff is an exchange of something desirable for something equally or more desirable. To make a tradeoff with a class you might say, "If you can get the paints put away before 11:00, we'll have time for the reading in pairs that you like to do so much."

* **Write a statement in which you make a reasonable tradeoff with a class or with an individual student.**

_____

_____

Offering choices to students suggests that you respect their ability to make decisions. Offering choices also develops in your pupils a feeling of owning and being responsible for the outcome of their selections. For instance, to offer your students an academic choice, you might suggest, "You may read any one of the following five books for your report. At the beginning of class tomorrow, I'll ask you for a slip of paper on which you've indicated your choice."

To offer a student a behavioral choice, you might say, "You may sit by your friend for now. If you don't distract others you can stay; if you do distract others you'll need to move to the far desk. It's your choice."

* **Write a statement in which you offer a student or the entire class acceptable choices.**

_____

_____

Honoring students' choices, even when we would have preferred that they make different ones, tells our students that their decisions will be respected. The pupil who chooses not to return his or her library books on time deserves to have the decision accepted (rather than labeled a "poor" choice). To honor a student's choice that doesn't agree with yours, you might say something like "You agreed that you would either stop distracting Akim or move to this desk. By distracting Akim, you have chosen to move. I respect your choice. Please move now."

* Write a statement in which you honor a student's negative choice, even though you may feel the choice was not the one he or she should have made.

_____

_____

Sending "I feel" messages lets teachers express their feelings about students' behavior while informing students what they can do to influence the teacher's mood. For example, telling a pupil, "I like your idea, Megan. At the same time, I feel worried that if we don't give Carlos a chance to talk now, we may miss his idea" is preferable to simply snapping, "Megan, stop interrupting." The latter will undoubtedly be interpreted as an attack, stimulating the desire for revenge. The following is an example of an "I feel" format:

I feel _____ when _____
               (feeling)   (something happens)

because _____
                                    (reason)

* Write an "I feel" message you could make to a student.

_____

_____

Some teachers prefer a slightly expanded form of the "I feel" message in which they also state how they will help. To send an "I feel" message in the expanded form, you might tell a student, "_I feel_ disappointed _when_ I see you not using the class time provided for getting started on your assignment _because_ I want you to know this material. _I'll help_ by checking your work on Problem 1 as soon as you finish it." In another situation, one might say, "_I feel_ annoyed _when_ I see others distracted by the rocking of your chair _because_ they have a right to learn without unnecessary distractions. _I'll help_ by permitting you to earn points by sitting still [or by allowing you to sit on the floor]." "I feel" messages tend to give students a feeling of control, because rather than demanding certain response, they allow a student to respond in his or her own way to the feeling stated.

* Write an "I feel" message in the expanded form.

_____

_____

Diverting attention from a potential problem can often reduce or avoid power struggles. In most cases, you can direct the pupil's attention away from a potentially negative situation toward a neutral or more positive activity. For instance, to defuse an argument beginning between two children, you might suggest, "Jake, can you please collect the bats and balls, and Erin, the bases? It's time to clean up and go inside."

* **Write a statement that would divert a student's attention away from a potential problem.**

_____

_____

Deferring part of a response to a student's misbehavior often prevents unnecessary embarrassment, benefiting the pupil's self-esteem. For example, you might say, "I feel angry when you deface the top of your desk. Please sit in this chair for now. We'll talk more, privately, when class is over."

* **Write a statement in which you defer part of a response to a student's misbehavior.**

_____

_____

If you are in a group learning situation, have each member choose one of their strategies for avoiding power struggles. In small groups, have each person share his or her strategy. * Provide constructive feedback to each other on the effectiveness of each strategy. List any suggestions for improvement.

1.

2.

SKILL: AVOIDING FEELINGS OF NEGLECT AND DISTRUST

An old adage says, "The squeaky wheel gets the grease." Some teachers give the lion's share of their attention to the most demanding pupils and, in doing so, ignore other children in the group. Children often do not understand why the teacher seems to be avoiding them, but they interpret it as rejection.

---

* If you are <u>not</u> in a group setting, elicit responses about what you have written from a family member, friend or colleague. If you do this for each skill in this skill group, you will gain additional insights about using each skill.

Feelings of neglect. Young people can easily experience *feelings of neglect* if left too much to their own devices. We can reduce such feelings by communicating real interest in the choices students make. In fact, studies show that it is not only the amount of *time* we give to the individual student, but the *interest* we show in their work that builds our relationship with them.

To make sure your pupils know you are concerned about the work they've been doing, you might say, "I have listed three alternative assignments on the board. You may choose the one that most interests you. I am interested in knowing which assignment you have selected, so tomorrow we'll spend a few minutes of class time discussing your selections."

* Write a statement that would show a student you are interested in his or her work.

_____

_____

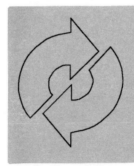

If you are in a group learning situation, in small groups have each person share his or her written statement. Provide constructive feedback to each other on the effectiveness of each statement. List any suggestions for improvement.

1.

2.

Feelings of distrust. Students tend to interpret too much teacher control as *distrust* of them. For example, a pupil would likely interpret the statement, "Don't sit on top of that desk—you might break it!" to mean "I'm concerned about the desk," when all the teacher really feels is concern for the student's safety. When you restrict or eliminate choices for students, let them know that you have their best interests at heart. You might say to the pupil sitting on the desk, "I worry when you sit on top of the desk. I'm afraid that it will collapse and you'll be hurt." Here the reason offered is related directly to the student's well-being.

* Write a statement that would show a student you have his or her best interests at heart.

_____

_____

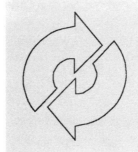

If you are in a group learning situation, in small groups have each person share his or her written statement. Provide constructive feedback to each other on the effectiveness of each statement. List any suggestions for improvement.

1.

2.

CONCLUDING STATEMENT

We can build self-esteem by encouraging students to make choices regarding their learning and behavior and by using other strategies to reduce power struggles. These techniques communicate to students that we believe they are capable of controlling aspects of their own lives.

QUESTIONS

Write your answers to the following questions on a separate piece of paper. Please indicate the grade level at which you teach.

Grade Level _____

1. Which skills or strategies from this skill group have you used successfully in your teaching?
2. What other skills or strategies related to giving children reasonable control should teachers know? Give examples of each.
3. Which of the skills or strategies for giving children reasonable control were most difficult for you to use? Why?
4. Which skills or strategies are particularly useful for children under the age of ten?
5. Which are particularly useful for children over the age of ten?
6. Which skills or strategies (if any) would you teach your students to use for the benefit of themselves and/or their classmates?
7. If you are in a group learning situation, select one of the above questions and share your response with your group members. Note reactions that might be helpful to you in future teaching.

REVIEW

Avoiding Power Struggles

• Offering trade-offs

"As soon as everyone has cleaned up their stations and quietly lined up at the door, we'll go to the playground."

• Offering choices

"We have enough baskets and space so that everyone can work on passing, dribbling, or shooting. With your partner, choose one of these activities and spend the first 10 minutes on it."

"You may choose to work for 15 minutes at one of the learning stations you haven't yet completed. The directions are at each station."

"You may begin the term by sitting next to your friend, but you'll have two choices: (1) you may choose not to disrupt those around you and continue to sit with Jon, or (2) you may choose to disrupt those around you and move to the empty chair over here. Please state your choices so that I know your understand them."

• Honoring negative choices

"You agreed that you would either stop pushing or go into time-out. By pushing again you have chosen time-out. Please come and sit over here."

• Sending "I feel" messages

"I feel angry when you disregard my requests for quiet because others cannot hear."

• Diverting attention from a potential problem

(To two youngsters whose wrestling in the pool began as fun but was becoming heated.) "Tony, I'd like you to practice your flip-turns at the shallow end of the pool; Aaron, let's have you work on your dives at the deep end."

• Deferring part of a response

"That behavior upsets me. I want you to take a three-minute time-out now; then see me before you go to lunch."

Avoiding Feelings of Neglect and Distrust

(Neglect) "You may choose one of the ten topics for your project. I'm interested in knowing which you have chosen."

(Distrust) "The reason I'd like you to finish your assignment in class is that a tutor can help you." ["It's not that I don't trust you to finish it at home."]

YOUR QUESTIONS

1. List at least two questions you have regarding the use of skills to give children reasonable control:
2. If you are in a group learning situation, share at least one of these questions with the members of your group. Note their responses and any insights gained.

FIELD APPLICATION

Plan, implement, and evaluate a method for investigating the effectiveness of one of the reasonable control skills included in this section with one or more of your students. The following is an example:

Let's say I decide to investigate using "I feel" messages rather than "you" messages. I choose to use "I feel" messages with Jacob, who has been mildly disruptive in the past two class periods. I plan to speak to Jacob privately after class when he is disruptive, and to record changes in his behavior in a journal for at least five days before employing other disciplinary means. I review my plan with colleagues.

Once I make modifications, I implement the plan. I record Jacob's responses after "I feel" messages (e.g., Jacob spoke more openly and calmly after I expressed how his talking with neighbors in class made me feel. Subsequently he was less disruptive).

When the five days are up, I review Jacob's responses and identify any patterns (for example, that Jacob was much less defensive when I used "I feel" messages during discussions of his disruptive behavior). I draw conclusions from my findings (e.g., that because "I feel" messages give students more control in determining their response to the sender of a disciplinary message, they tend to de-escalate hostile feelings toward the sender).

I share my findings, conclusions, and recommendations with teachers, parents, and other appropriate persons. In doing so, I protect the anonymity of my students.

The following outline is provided as a guide for planning, implementing, and evaluating your personal action plan for using the skills related to giving students feelings of reasonable control.

I. **Plan** your investigation by answering the following questions.

1. Which skill from this section will you investigate?
2. Which students will participate in your study?
3. How and when will you use the skill?
4. How will you remind yourself to practice the skill frequently?
5. How will you monitor your use of the skill?
6. What method will you use to record changes in your students' behavior that seem to result from your application of the skill?
7. How long will your investigation last?
8. Discuss your plan with one or two colleagues. What suggestions did they provide for improving your study?

II. **Implement** your field application plan. Record each time you use the skill and each student response to its use.

III. **Evaluate** your study.

1. Analyze your data and identify any patterns.
2. List the major findings and conclusions of your study.
3. List for other teachers at your grade level recommendations for using the skill.
4. Share what you have learned with others.

Now, if necessary, modify your approach and replicate your study. Then repeat the study using other skills for giving reasonable control with your students.

*   *   *

SKILL GROUP FOUR:
REINFORCING STUDENTS AS LOVABLE AND CAPABLE

A fourth way of building self-esteem in young people is to reinforce them as both lovable and capable. Students need to be told and shown that we love them unconditionally, that is, we consider them inherently worthy of love regardless of what they can do. They also need to be told and shown that they are capable—of mastering tasks, making decisions, solving problems, caring for others. The purpose of this skill group is to identify ways to show students that they are lovable and capable academically, socially, physically, and emotionally.

**Objective: To know and be able to apply skills
for reinforcing children as lovable and capable.**

SKILL: OFFERING SPECIFIC ENCOURAGEMENT AND PRAISE *

Many adults have a tendency to simply respond "Good!" to almost everything students do. Such indiscriminate feedback does not really help children because it does not tell them which aspect of their behavior is being admired. Moreover, such vague praise does not build self-esteem because young people soon realize that terms like "good" are used widely (and without meaning) by adults who don't take the time to notice unique and special aspects of an accomplishment.

Specific reinforcement statements, such as "I like your selection of colors and your broad strokes," tell students that you really noticed details of their performance.

A specific statement of encouragement or praise may be followed by a positive generalization regarding a student's overall talent or ability if warranted: "I like your selection of colors and your broad strokes. You are good at painting."

---

* By "praise," we mean a "positive response to a student's trait, ability, performance, or effort that goes beyond mere positive feedback about correctness." Responses such as "You're right," or "That answer is correct," or "Yes" are not considered praise. (Adapted from J. Brophy, "On Praising Effectively," *Elementary School Journal*, Vol. 81, No. 5, 1981.)

* **Write a statement of encouragement or praise in which a specific compliment is followed by a positive generalization about your student's ability, achievement, or effort.**

_____

_____

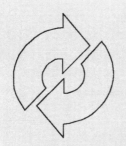

If you are in a group learning situation, in small groups have each person share his or her written statement. * Provide constructive feedback to each other on the effectiveness of each statement. List any suggestions for improvement.

1.

2.

SKILL: BEING SPECIFIC ABOUT NEGATIVE BEHAVIOR

As teachers we sometimes need to correct inadequate work or negative behavior. In doing so, we should avoid making vague judgments like "That's too messy; you should be neater" or "Your margins are poor." Such criticism will not tell students what was wrong with their work or behavior, and they may think we are condemning their general worth. Instead we should be clear and specific in our criticism: "Please make your left margin an inch wider."

We should also avoid condemnatory generalizations about negative behavior: "You are always so sloppy!" Instead, we need to be specific about unacceptable behavior: "Please remember to put your supplies neatly in your box for next class."

* **Write a statement in which you generalize about a student's inadequate work or negative behavior.**

_____

_____

* **Now convert that statement into one that focuses specifically on the work or behavior.**

_____

_____

---

* If you are <u>not</u> in a group setting, elicit responses about what you have written from a family member, friend or colleague. If you do this for each skill in this skill group, you will gain additional insights about using each skill.

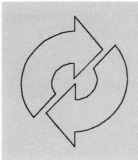

If you are in a group learning situation, in small groups have each person share his or her written statements. Provide constructive feedback to each other on the effectiveness of the statements. List any suggestions for improvement.

1.

2.

SKILL: SEPARATING THE BEHAVIOR FROM THE PERSON

When trying to give a student an honest critical response, we often fail to separate clearly the performance from the person. Statements like "That was not very smart!" or "Nice girls don't act like that!" or "Bad boy!" or "Man, are you lazy," can affect self-esteem negatively because they focus criticism on the person rather than the behavior.

When disciplining a student, you can separate the behavior from the person by saying something like, "You know that I like you and enjoy having you sit with us. However, I disapprove of you distracting Jenny from her homework. If you don't stop, you'll be choosing to go to the time-out room. Do you understand?"

* Write a statement that does not separate the behavior from the person.

_____

_____

* Now convert that statement into one that separates the behavior from the person.

_____

_____

If you are in a group learning situation, in small groups have each person share his or her written statements. Provide constructive feedback to each other on the effectiveness of the statements. List any suggestions for improvement.

1.

2.

SKILL: HELPING STUDENTS AVOID GENERALIZING NEGATIVE MESSAGES

Students tend to generalize the negative. For example, after getting a low score on a spelling quiz, they may conclude, "I am terrible in English" or "I can never do anything right." We can counter that tendency by reminding the pupil to look at the whole picture: "I know you feel disappointed in your grade [empathy statement]. It's true that you didn't do well on this spelling quiz, but you usually get better scores. Besides, you're a great reader. That doesn't make you 'terrible in English' in my book!"

Another technique is to encourage a student to see the broader picture by asking open questions, such as "In what parts of your English class have you done well?" Helping them to come to their own conclusion is usually preferable to telling them that they are wrong to generalize.

* **Write a statement that would help counter a student's tendency to generalize negative messages.**

_____

_____

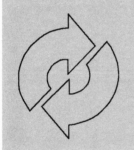

If you are in a group learning situation, in small groups have each person share his or her written statement. Provide constructive feedback to each other on the effectiveness of each statement. List any suggestions for improvement.

1.

2.

SKILL: REINFORCING EFFORT

If we want students to keep trying, we must reward effort. Even when pupils' attempts are not fully successful, we can still reinforce their willingness to try. You might say something like, "Kendra, you worked hard on your homework for tomorrow. I like that." Even when a student succeeds, you should reinforce effort. "Your high test score is not due to luck—your hard work paid off!"

* Write a statement reinforcing a student for putting forth an honest effort.

_____

_____

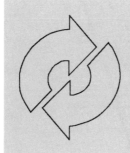

If you are in a group learning situation, in small groups have each person share his or her written statement. Provide constructive feedback to each other on the effectiveness of each statement. List any suggestions for improvement.

1.

2.

SKILL: REINFORCING RISK-TAKING

Psychologists (Bednar et al., 1989) suggest that risk-taking develops feelings of competence. Being able to invite conditions known to be accompanied by some psychological threat enhances feelings of being lovable and capable.

To reinforce risk-taking, you might simply suggest, "I like it when you use innovative strategies—nice going!" or "You tried a new way this time—how'd you like it?" The first example provides external judgment; the second encourages internal evaluation. For younger students, including your judgment is appropriate; for older children, encouraging self-evaluation is preferable.

* Write a statement that rewards academic or social risk-taking in students at your grade level.

_____

_____

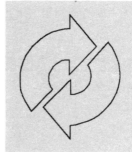

If you are in a group learning situation, in small groups have each person share his or her written statement. Provide constructive feedback to each other on the effectiveness of each statement. List any suggestions for improvement.

1.

2.

SKILL: REINFORCING TAKING PERSONAL RESPONSIBILITY

Studies (Bednar et al., 1989) also suggest that when people take personal responsibility for causes and consequences of their behavior, they feel more capable of coping and, therefore, generally feel more lovable and capable.

To reinforce students who take personal responsibility for academic and/or social behavior, we might say, "Do you feel that you contributed to the high score of your team?" "What effect did your statement have on the others in your group?" or "Your input made a tremendous difference to the outcome of your cooperative learning project!" For younger students including your judgment is appropriate; for older students, encouraging more self-evaluation is preferable.

* **Write a statement that reinforces a student at your grade level for taking personal responsibility.**

_____

_____

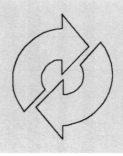

If you are in a group learning situation, in small groups have each person share his or her written statement. Provide constructive feedback to each other on the effectiveness of each statement. List any suggestions for improvement.

1.

2.

SKILL: REINFORCING IMPROVEMENT

In the past some teachers rewarded only those students who did well when compared with others. We now know that evaluating performance strictly on the basis of how one student compares with another is neither as effective nor as humane as evaluating individuals on the basis of their own past performance.

If we want a student to improve, we need to reward improvement. Even when achievements are not yet what we know they can be, we can nevertheless note progress over past performance.

To reinforce improvement, you might say something like, "Naomi, you completed the flash cards in four minutes today. Yesterday it took you four minutes and forty-five seconds. That's quite an improvement!"

* Write a statement that reinforces a student at your grade level for individual improvement.

_____

_____

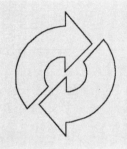

If you are in a group learning situation, in small groups have each person share his or her written statement. Provide constructive feedback to each other on the effectiveness of each statement. List any suggestions for improvement.

1.

2.

SKILL: REINFORCING ACCOMPLISHMENTS
OF WHICH STUDENTS MAY NOT BE AWARE

We need to reinforce students' less obvious as well as their obvious accomplishments. We must identify positive behaviors that, however small, allow us to begin encouraging improvement. To reinforce minor improvement, you might say something like, "Danny, I noticed that you cleaned the hamster's cage. Good for you." or "Thanks for inviting our new classmate to join your game. That was kind of you."

* Write a statement that reinforces a student for a less obvious achievement.

_____

_____

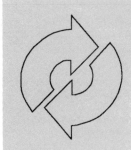

If you are in a group learning situation, in small groups have each person share his or her written statement. Provide constructive feedback to each other on the effectiveness of each statement. List any suggestions for improvement.

1.

2.

SKILL: REINFORCING FEELINGS OF BEING LOVABLE

Most of the skills described so far relate more to feelings of being capable than to feelings of being lovable. And especially for young students, feeling capable does give rise to feeling lovable. However, we must be careful not to imply that students are worthy only when they perform well. Although we need to reward them for performance so they'll continue to learn, we also need to reward them for who they are regardless of what they can do. To reinforce pupils for "being" (as opposed to "doing"), we can say, "I'm glad you're in my class," or "I enjoy your company."

* Write a statement reinforcing a student at your grade level for being lovable.

_____

_____

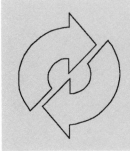

If you are in a group learning situation, in small groups have each person share his or her written statement. Provide constructive feedback to each other on the effectiveness of each statement. List any suggestions for improvement.

1.

2.

CONCLUDING STATEMENT

Using these reinforcement skills will help teach a child that he or she is lovable and capable. We need to remember that encouragement and praise should be intended to show appreciation or to give specific information—not to manipulate or control a classroom. A statement like, "Look how nicely Angie is sitting" will likely be interpreted by Angie as an attempt to use her to control the class rather than to reward her. One way to avoid misinterpretation of intent is to give certain encouragement or praise in private. While some public praise is beneficial to certain (especially some lower elementary) students, for middle childhood and adolescent students, as well as students of certain cultural backgrounds, public praise may be embarrassing and demeaning.

Although we should readily reinforce even small improvements, we should refrain from rewarding insincerely. Rewards for *capabilities* must be earned, or pupils will not experience the sense of accomplishment that comes from real effort or progress. Reinforcement for *lovability* should be unconditional.

Finally, if we want students to become self-motivating, we need to praise them for being self-motivated. Using extrinsic rewards may indeed be critical for some students. Once students are motivated, however, we should move toward rewarding their internal drives: "I'm glad you see this is important." and "You seem to enjoy this lesson."

Whether externally or internally focused or given publicly or privately, specific encouragement or praise—given sincerely and based on real accomplishment—will benefit students' self-esteem.

QUESTIONS

Write your answers to the following questions on a separate piece of paper. Please indicate the grade level at which you teach.

Grade Level _____

1. Which of the reinforcement skills have worked best for you?
2. What other reinforcement skills should teachers know and practice regularly? Why?
3. Do you agree with the hypothesis that if students do not get their need for belonging, attention, and self-esteem met though positive (socially approved) means, they will seek to have them met through negative (deviant) means? Why or why not?
4. What reinforcement systems have worked for you? (one example of a reinforcement system would be adding a kernel of corn to a jar every time one of your students helps another, then having a class popcorn party when the jar is filled.)
5. How can you teach your students to reward friends and siblings?
6. If you are in a group learning situation, select one of the above questions and share your response with your group members. Note reactions that might be helpful to you in future teaching.

REVIEW

Offering Specific Encouragement and Praise

(Nonspecific) "Well done."
(Specific) "Your paper is well-organized, concise, and neatly written. In addition, you related your interest to what we've been doing in class. You described two alternate approaches to the problem and then gave your evaluation of each. I especially like. . ."

Being Specific about Negative Behavior

(Nonspecific) "Every time I see you, you're running."
(Specific) "Please walk."

(Nonspecific) "You always forget to sharpen your pencil before class. Don't you ever listen?"
(Specific) "Please sharpen your pencil."

(Nonspecific) "You're always bothering someone; stop it."
(Specific) "Please stop talking to Maria."

Separating the Behavior from the Person

(No Separation) "You're lazy and irresponsible."
(Separation) "You need to complete the duties on this list; please clean your lab area."

(No Separation) "Good girls [boys] don't push."
(Separation) "Pushing makes me worry that someone might get hurt."

(No Separation) "You are being awful today."
(Separation) "Shoving other students is unkind. It's not like you to do that—you can either stop it or lose your recess privilege for today."

Helping Students Avoid Generalizing Negative Messages

(Child) "I'm a failure."
(Teacher) [paraphrasing] "You feel that you can't do anything right today? What specifically has gone wrong?" [after empathizing and discussing feelings] "Does losing your pencil and getting a C on a math quiz mean you're a failure?" [If the child says, "Yes," you might cite examples of the child's successes on other days or even state directly that in your opinion the difficulties experienced don't mean he or she is a failure].

Reinforcing Effort

"You got 8 out of 10 correct, and on this quiz that was not easy. I like your effort—you studied hard."

"I like the way you've made Jamie feel at home by asking him to join you at lunch. That was considerate. Thanks."

Reinforcing Risk-Taking

"You took a risk sharing that idea in class—it would have been easier to go along with the others. Nice going!"

Reinforcing Taking Personal Responsibility

"You accepted responsibility for that accomplishment [or misbehavior]. I admire that!"

Reinforcing Improvement

"By correcting the four problems you missed yesterday, you have improved your score by two points."

[privately] "You spoke out of turn only once today. That's quite an improvement. You must feel good about your progress, right?"

"Thanks for holding the door for Kirsten. I like your helpful attitude!"

Reinforcing Accomplishments of Which Students May Not Be Aware

"Your positive outlook on life helps those around you. I like your optimism."

Reinforcing Feelings of Being Lovable

"You're fun to be around."

YOUR QUESTIONS

1. List at least two questions you have regarding the use of skills for reinforcing students as lovable and capable.
2. If you are in a group learning situation, share at least one of these questions with the members of your group. Note any insights gained.

FIELD APPLICATION

Plan, implement, and evaluate a method for investigating the effectiveness of one of the reinforcing skills with one or more of your students. The following is an example:

Let's say I decide to study the effects of reinforcing students for improvement in perseverance. I pick as my subject Ryan, an unmotivated but able fifth grader. I decide to reinforce privately after class over the next two weeks and record his responses to my reinforcement in a journal. I place a reminder to "reinforce improvement" in my grade book. I review my plan with colleagues.

Once I make final modifications, I implement the plan. I record each time I use the skill and each of Ryan's responses (when I told Ryan, "You revised that passage several times. You stuck with it longer than in the past—I admire your perseverance," Ryan responded with a big smile, saying, "Yeah, I'm glad I kept trying, 'cause now I like what I wrote.")

When the two weeks are up, I review Ryan's responses and identify any patterns (e.g., that Ryan's perseverance increased slightly for four days in a row). I draw conclusions from my findings (e.g., that reinforcing perseverance seems to foster student confidence).

I share my findings, conclusions, and recommendations with teachers, parents, and other appropriate persons. In doing so, I protect the anonymity of my students.

The following outline is provided as a guide for planning, implementing, and evaluating an action plan for using skills for reinforcing children.

I. **Plan** your investigation by answering the following questions:

1. Which skill from this section will you investigate?
2. Which student(s) will participate in your study?
3. How and when will you use the skill?

4. How will you remind yourself to practice the skill frequently?
5. How will you monitor your use of the skill?
6. What method will you use to record changes in students' behavior that seem to result from your application of the skill?
7. How long will your investigation last?
8. Discuss your plan with one or two colleagues. What suggestions did they provide for improving your study?

II. **Implement** your field application plan. Record each time you use the skill and each student's response to its use.

III. **Evaluate** your study:

1. Analyze your data and identify any patterns.
2. List the major findings and conclusions of your study.
3. List recommendations for using the skill.
4. Share your recommendations with others.

Now, if necessary, modify your approach and replicate your study. Then repeat the study using other skills for reinforcing students as lovable and capable.

*   *   *

A child's life is like a piece of paper on which every passerby leaves a mark.

— Ancient Chinese Proverb

SKILL GROUP FIVE:
MODELING A POSITIVE VIEW OF YOURSELF

Objective: To know and be able to apply
skills for modeling a positive view of yourself.

Young people learn a great deal through imitation. Children and youth can learn to view themselves positively by seeing others demonstrate a positive view of themselves. Self-esteem, in a sense, can be caught.

Teachers are among the most influential people in the lives of young people. The purpose of this skill group is to learn how, through modeling, you can effectively help students gain self-esteem.

SKILL: TALKING POSITIVELY ABOUT YOURSELF

In contemporary American society, we are taught to keep to ourselves our virtues, successes, and achievements, for such talk seems boastful and suggests a lack of humility. However, young people need to see that you value your accomplishments and yourself. If they do, they feel justified in valuing their accomplishments and themselves. By acknowledging our positive attributes, we encourage students to acknowledge theirs without guilt or pretension.

One way to model self-confidence to your pupils is by speaking positively about yourself and your accomplishments. A statement like "Yeah, I think I'm a pretty good teacher and, what's more, I think teaching is the most important of all professions!" suggests justifiable pride in oneself as a professional.

* Write a positive statement about yourself you could share with your students.

_____

_____

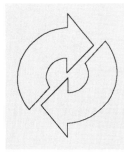

If you are in a group learning situation, in small groups have each person share his or her written statement. * Provide constructive feedback to each other on the effectiveness of each statement. List any suggestions for improvement.

1.

2.

SKILL: COMMUNICATING THAT YOU CAN ADMIT MISTAKES AND REBOUND FROM THEM

Some people live their lives desperately trying not to fail. They are so attuned to avoiding failure they do not take the risks that successful living requires.

For many, mistakes connote failure, and these people regard all mistakes as the result of weakness and incompetence. In actuality, the willingness to make mistakes is vital for learning. Newton's laws of motion or Einstein's theory of relativity never would have emerged without some mistakes and rethinking along the way.

We can model self-esteem by letting students know not only that we make mistakes but that we can rebound from them. Making statements like "One simple mistake threw me off, but I've got a handle on it now!" or "It slowed me down, but it sure didn't stop me!" communicates that you can err without being devastated in the process.

* **Write a statement that informs students about a mistake you made that did not destroy your self-esteem.**

_____

_____

---

* If you are <u>not</u> in a group setting, elicit responses about what you have written from a family member, friend or colleague. If you do this for each skill in this skill group, you will gain additional insights about using each skill.

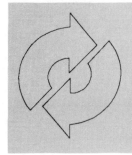

If you are in a group learning situation, in small groups have each person share his or her written statement. Provide constructive feedback to each other on the effectiveness of each statement. List any suggestions for improvement.

1.

2.

SKILL: TAKING REASONABLE RISKS

Just as we need to reinforce risk-taking in students, we need to communicate to our students that teachers are confident enough to take reasonable risks, that is, to try new things. To do this, you might relate to your pupils the progress you are making in a home or school project. You could say, for example, "I'm going to try to install a stereo radio in my son's car today. It should be interesting; I've never done it before." Another example might be, "I'm going to dress up as a chocolate chip cookie for Halloween."

* **Write a statement you could share with your students in which you show a willingness to take reasonable risks.**

_____

_____

If you are in a group learning situation, in small groups have each person share his or her written statement. Provide constructive feedback to each other on the effectiveness of each statement. List any suggestions for improvement.

1.

2.

SKILL: COMMUNICATING THAT HELPING OTHERS BENEFITS ONE'S OWN SELF-ESTEEM

We all know how good it makes us feel to help others. If we can provide students with an opportunity to help others—in class or in school or through community service activities—they too may feel more worthy.

We can model healthy self-esteem by letting our students know how we have used our talents and abilities to aid others, and how doing so has made us feel good. You might say, "I'm glad I was able to help Ms. Wong with her lab setup. It makes me happy when I can be useful to another teacher and her class."

* **Write a statement that communicates to a student how you have recently used an ability or talent to help another person.**

_____

_____

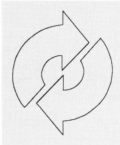

If you are in a group learning situation, in small groups have each person share his or her written statement. Provide constructive feedback to each other on the effectiveness of each statement. List any suggestions for improvement.

1.

2.

SKILL: CONVERTING PUT-DOWNS TO STATEMENTS OF SELF-APPROVAL

Society has taught us that to be properly humble we must identify our shortcomings and minimize our strengths. If we are to demonstrate how to feel lovable and capable to students, however, we must limit derogatory statements and make some statements of self-approval. Remarks like "I'm so forgetful" or "I'm just a teacher" can be converted to statements of self-approval, for example, "I'm getting pretty good at remembering names" or "I'm proud to be a teacher."

* **Write a "put-down" of yourself you have made to your students.**

_____

_____

* **Now convert that statement into a self-enhancing one.**

_____

_____

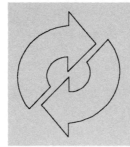

If you are in a group learning situation, in small groups have each person share his or her written statement. Provide constructive feedback to each other on the effectiveness of each statement. List any suggestions for improvement.

1.

2.

SKILL: MODELING PERSISTENCE

Because persistence at a task often leads to success, we need to demonstrate that we have the persistence we need to solve problems and complete tasks. We can model persistence by keeping at a task and by saying things like "Let me attack this from another angle. I know I can get it" or "I'm going to keep trying. I know I can do it."

* **Write a statement that demonstrates you have the persistence to succeed at a task.**

_____

_____

If you are in a group learning situation, in small groups have each person share his or her written statement. Provide constructive feedback to each other on the effectiveness of each statement. List any suggestions for improvement.

1.

2.

SKILL: IDENTIFYING TRAITS/INTERESTS COMMON TO YOU AND YOUR STUDENTS

We need to inform students, privately or publicly, that we possess traits, talents, abilities, and interests similar to theirs. For example, we could say, "Sandy, you have a real love for music. I enjoy music too" or "I used to be afraid of the dark, too" or "You're good with people—I've always enjoyed socializing as well."

* **Write a statement that would illustrate to a student that he or she has a positive trait, talent, ability, or interest you also possess.**

_____

_____

If you are in a group learning situation, in small groups have each person share his or her written statement. Provide constructive feedback to each other on the effectiveness of each statement. List any suggestions for improvement.

1.

2.

CONCLUDING STATEMENT

We can foster self-esteem in students by modeling that we are lovable and capable. Talking positively about ourselves, demonstrating resilience, taking reasonable risks, helping others, eliminating self-destructive statements, demonstrating persistence, and identifying positive attributes common to you and your students are all ways of communicating that we feel lovable and capable.

QUESTIONS

Write your answers to the following questions on a separate piece of paper. Please indicate the grade level at which you teach.

Grade Level _____

1. Which of the modeling techniques have you used successfully in your classroom?
2. List other skills and strategies that a teacher can and should use to model good self-esteem.
3. Which of the skills would you be willing to practice and use more?
4. How could you teach your students to model that they feel lovable and capable to classmates?
5. If you are in a group learning situation, select one of the above questions and share your response with your group members. Note reactions that might be helpful to you in future teaching.

REVIEW

Talking Positively about Yourself

> "I have a gift of. . ."
> "I'm pretty good at. . ."
> "I'm getting better at. . ."
> "I've worked hard to improve my. . ."

Communicating That You Can Admit Mistakes and Rebound from Them

> "Even though I didn't do so well on my last assignment in my education course, I'm certain that with extra credit work I'll still learn what I want to learn and at the same time get a good grade."

Taking Reasonable Risks

> "This summer I designed and helped build a deck on the back of our house. It was my first try at deck carpentry and the deck turned out well."

Communicating That Helping Others Benefits One's Own Self-Esteem

> "I helped our neighbor sew some new clothes this weekend. It sure feels good to help others."

Converting Put-Downs to Statements of Self-Approval

> (Rather than "I can't do anything right.") "I'm just having a bad day. I can usually do this with ease—I think I'll leave it for now and finish tomorrow."

Modeling Persistence

> "Though I'll put this problem off till morning, I'm not giving up!"

Identifying Traits/Interests Common to You and Your Students

> "You're good at collecting and organizing those baseball cards. I've always been a collector. I still have books in which I mounted cards, stickers, and stamps when I was in junior high."

> "I had the same trouble for a long time. I always had to think twice about where the decimal was supposed to go."

> "I see you enjoy humor. I've always enjoyed a good laugh myself."

YOUR QUESTIONS

1. List at least two questions you have regarding the use of skills for modeling a positive view of yourself.
2. If you are in a group learning situation, share at least one of these questions with the members of your group. Note their responses and any insights gained.

FIELD APPLICATION

Plan, implement, and evaluate a method for investigating the effectiveness of one of the skills for modeling a positive view of yourself with one or more of your students. The following is an example:

Let's say I decide to investigate the effects of communicating to my students that I have the ability and the talent to help others, and that doing so builds my self-confidence. Several times a week, I will share with all my students examples of my helping others and how helping them made me feel. I decide to record student responses in a notebook. I review my plan with colleagues.

Once I make final modifications, I implement the plan. I record each time I share a service experience and student responses to my experience (e.g., smiles and nods, students' stories of similar experiences and the positive feelings they had about them).

When the four weeks are up, I review student responses and identify any patterns (e.g., that each day I shared a service experience, a student would also share one, or that students began to speak of their service experiences more positively over the four weeks). I draw conclusions from my findings (e.g., that sharing service experiences encourages students to recall their own service to others and to feel good about themselves as a result).

I share my findings, conclusions, and recommendations with teachers, parents, and other appropriate persons. In doing so I protect the anonymity of my students.

The following set of questions is provided as a guide for planning, implementing, and evaluating an action plan for applying the skills related to modeling a positive view of yourself.

    I. **Plan** your investigation by answering the following questions.

        1. What skill from this section will you investigate?
        2. Which students will participate in your study?
        3. How and when will you use the skill?
        4. How will you remind yourself to practice the skill frequently?
        5. How will you monitor your use of the skill?
        6. What method will you use to record the changes in your students' behavior that result from your application of the skill?
        7. How long will your investigation last?
        8. Discuss your plan with one or two colleagues. What suggestions did they provide for improving your study?

    II. **Implement** your field application plan.

    III. **Evaluate** your study.

        1. Analyze your data and identify patterns (if any) in that data.
        2. List the major findings and conclusions of your study.
        3. List recommendations for other teachers at your grade level for using the skill you employed.
        4. Share the results of your study with others.

Now, if necessary, modify your approach and replicate your study. Then repeat the study using other skills for modeling a positive view of yourself to students.

*   *   *

Part II:

Strategies for
Building Self-Esteem

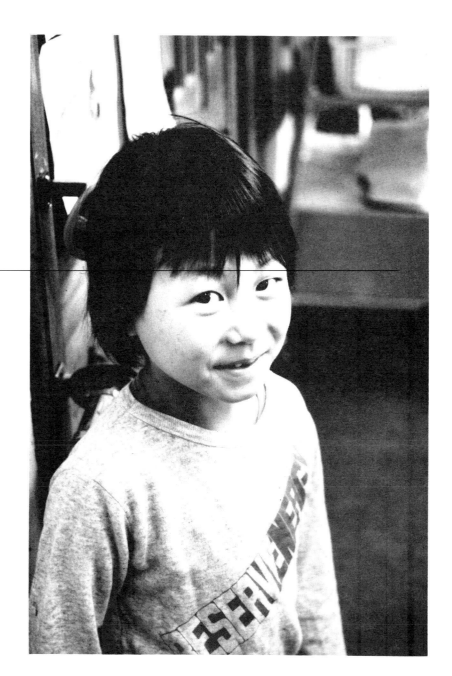

Searching
  looking for answers
    an identity
Always
  reaching outside ourselves.
Risking.
  Trusting.
    Sharing.
No answers
  only questions
    tests and pain
      curiosity.
If only a bit of light
  a piece of glass
    a reflecting crystal
to look back within
  and find the answers
    to the searching.

                    — Maile Topliff

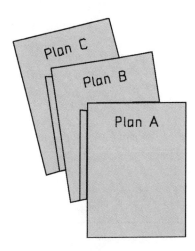

PROVEN STRATEGIES FOR APPLYING
SELF-ESTEEM PRINCIPLES IN THE CLASSROOM

The following pages contain lists of ways in which teachers have successfully applied each of the self-esteem principles to their particular classrooms. You have probably employed a number of these strategies yourself. These lists are designed to help you identify additional techniques.

STRATEGIES FOR LISTENING TO AND ACKNOWLEDGING STUDENTS' THOUGHTS AND FEELINGS

1. Focus attention on the student; do not allow unnecessary interruptions.

2. Discuss good listening skills with students. Ask them questions like "How do you feel when someone doesn't listen to you?" "What can you do to show someone that you are listening?"

3. Organize sharing time, that is, a period during which students know they have your permission and encouragement to discuss anything on their minds.

4. Accept the parts of students' statements that are correct in order to help them clarify and correct their responses. Seek explanations of how students arrived at their answers.

5. Establish "brainstorming" guidelines for selected activities so children know that their contributions will be accepted as valid and not judged as right or wrong.

6. Give students opportunities to express thoughts and feelings in ways other than oral, e.g., through writing journals and suggestion sheets, drawing sketches, role-playing, drama, and puppetry.

7. Use open-ended questions whenever possible to reduce students' fear of right and wrong answers, e.g., "How might you personally interpret the short poem, John?"

8. Invite students to design or modify assigned tasks to suit their own needs and interests.

9. Invite students' responses to classroom policies and procedures through written questionnaires. Use the results to alter your approach. If you cannot modify your method, acknowledge your pupils' suggestions.

10. Teach students how to assertively request that others listen to and acknowledge their thoughts and feelings.

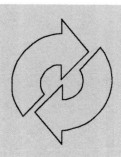

* List by number each of the above strategies that has worked well for you.

_____

_____

* List by number each of the above strategies you have not used that would be appropriate to use with your students.

_____

_____

* List by number which of these strategies you would be willing to try in your classroom.

_____

_____

* What strategies other than those presented above have helped you employ the skill of listening to and acknowledging thoughts and feelings?

_____

_____

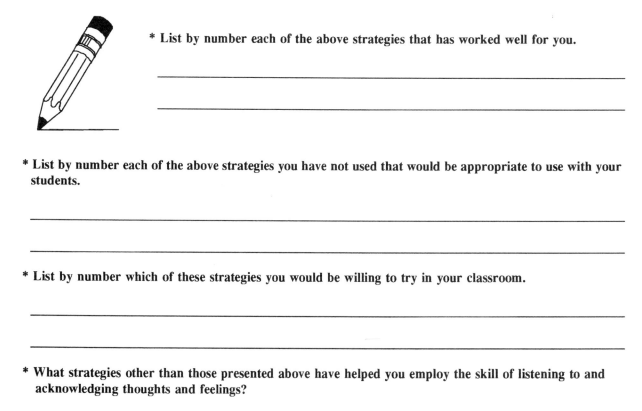

If you are in a group learning situation, discuss the written responses you have entered above. Invite suggestions from colleagues on how to improve and expand your list of strategies in this area. * List insights gained.

1.

2.

* If you are <u>not</u> in a group setting, elicit responses about what you have written from a family member, friend or colleague. If you do this for each skill in this skill group, you will gain additional insights about using each skill.

STRATEGIES FOR STRUCTURING FOR STUDENT SUCCESS

1. Clearly specify the limits of student choice regarding specific learning goals, methods of study, and means for evaluating a given task. For example, "Your project must focus on some aspect of Afro-American culture, include at least one review of a piece of literature, and result in some new insights for your classmates."

2. Teach students the skills for structuring their own situations for success.

3. Provide examples of what is expected.

4. Break down assignments into small steps. Check (and reward) student progress at each step to ensure that students are moving in the right general direction.

5. Simplify introductory exercises to enable more students to succeed.

6. Use varied illustrations to meet the different learning styles of students. (e.g., for secondary students use both sequential and random ordering and provide both concrete and abstract examples).

7. Show students how to ask their own questions regarding relevant issues and problems.

8. Use cooperative learning activities in which students help each other succeed.

9. Define and post a list of class rules; rules should be short, clear, and stated positively.

10. Arrange your room physically to minimize obstacles to learning and to maximize learning. For example, seat students so all can see the teacher and the board, and, when necessary, so that disruptive pupils are separated.

11. Provide options that vary in degree of difficulty, allowing students to choose exercises that fit their particular ability level.

12. Insist that students record only positive or constructive comments in their peer evaluations of work of classmates.

13. Sometimes group students of different abilities together so they can experience both helping and being helped in a variety of mental and physical tasks.

14. To accentuate the positive, mark correct answers on assignments rather than wrong answers.

15. In classes such as home economics, social studies, health, and physical education, discuss the importance of self-esteem and explain how to develop it at both the elementary and secondary levels. Include skills and strategies that students can use to enhance their own and their peers' self-esteem.

16. Rotate teams and small groups so that students work in cooperative ways with a variety of students of different cultural, gender and disability backgrounds.

* List by number each of the above strategies that has worked well for you.

_____

_____

* List by number each of the above strategies you have not used that would be appropriate to use with your students.

_____

_____

* List by number which of these strategies you would be willing to try in your classroom.

_____

_____

* What strategies other than those presented above have helped you structure your classroom for success?

_____

_____

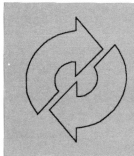

If you are in a group learning situation, discuss the written responses you have entered above. Invite suggestions from colleagues on how to improve and expand your expertise in this area. List insights gained.

1.

2.

STRATEGIES FOR GIVING STUDENTS FEELINGS OF REASONABLE CONTROL

1. Provide alternative activities in the classroom so that students can choose, for example, among different learning stations, worksheets, or reading materials.

2. Allow students to help plan their own classroom parties, games, treats, etc.

3. Encourage students to help formulate class rules.

4. Grant students some choice regarding specific learning goals, methods of study, and methods of evaluation. Permit them, for example, to alter the direction of a project underway.

5. Give students the opportunity to "pass" on portions of classroom activities.

6. Within limits, allow students to determine how they'll spend their free time.

7. Allow a few minutes at the beginning of each class for students to expend energy or express feelings.

8. Allow students the option of retaking tests or redoing assignments to improve their scores.

9. Develop with students individualized learning contracts that include choices regarding specific objectives, methods of study, and methods of evaluating outcomes.

10. Allow students to take on leadership roles in class.

11. Provide opportunities for students to do extra credit.

12. Allow students to eliminate one test grade from each grading period.

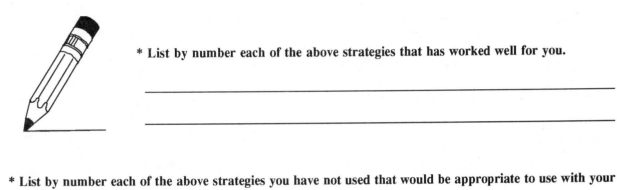

* List by number each of the above strategies that has worked well for you.

_____

_____

* List by number each of the above strategies you have not used that would be appropriate to use with your students.

_____

_____

* List by number which of these strategies you would be willing to try in your classroom.

_____

_____

* What strategies other than those presented above have helped you employ the skill of giving children reasonable control?

_____

_____

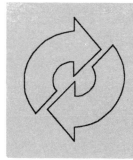

If you are in a group learning situation, discuss the written responses you have entered above. Invite suggestions from colleagues on how to improve and expand your expertise in this area. List insights gained.

1.

2.

STRATEGIES FOR REINFORCING STUDENTS AS LOVABLE AND CAPABLE

1. Praise and encourage students conditionally for being capable, i.e., only when they have improved at something or exerted an honest effort; praise and encourage them unconditionally for being lovable.

2. When acknowledging low performance, identify some aspect of the performance that was positive, e.g., "You had more [tennis] serves in bounds today than you had yesterday. You could improve on . . . Your follow-through, however, was very good today."

3. Teach students to encourage and praise each other, not only for positive behaviors but also for personal attributes including ethnic and cultural associations.

4. Teach students to use the reinforcing skills described in this workbook to reinforce themselves.

5. Teach students how to record and monitor their accomplishments in a journal, log or chart.

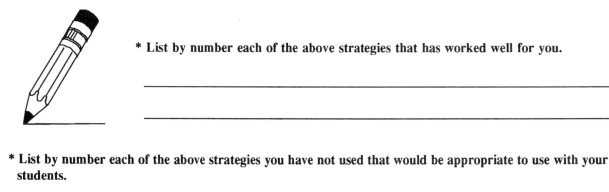

* List by number each of the above strategies that has worked well for you.

_____

_____

* List by number each of the above strategies you have not used that would be appropriate to use with your students.

_____

_____

* List by number which of these strategies you would be willing to try in your classroom.

_____

_____

* **What strategies other than those presented above have helped you reinforce students as lovable and capable?**

_____

_____

If you are in a group learning situation, discuss the written responses you have entered above. Invite suggestions from colleagues on how to improve and expand your expertise in this area. List insights gained.

1.

2.

STRATEGIES FOR MODELING A POSITIVE VIEW OF YOURSELF

1. Share pictures and other symbols of your own accomplishments where you display students accomplishments (bulletin board, hallways, etc).

2. Take a turn on the "student-of-the-week" board; share pictures and other symbols of your accomplishments.

3. To demonstrate persistence in solving problems, tell students about a problem that you worked hard at and solved. Also let them observe you in the process of solving problems.

4. Identify others—public figures or associates—who have overcome obstacles. Be sure to include positive models of different cultural, gender and disability backgrounds.

5. Enlist students in cooperative projects in the classroom, in which you can demonstrate your talents and abilities.

6. Display a sense of humor regarding your strengths and limitations.

* **List by number each of the above strategies that has worked well for you.**

_____

_____

* **List by number each of the above strategies you have not used that would be appropriate
to use with your students.**

_____

_____

* **List by number which of these strategies you would be willing to try in your classroom.**

_____

_____

* **What strategies other than those presented above have helped you model a positive view of yourself?**

_____

_____

If you are in a group learning situation, discuss the written responses you have entered above. Invite suggestions from colleagues on how to improve and expand your expertise in this area. List insights gained.

1.

2.

*   *   *

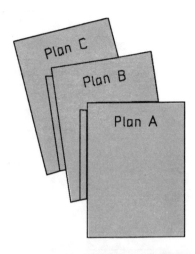

DESIGNING A PERSONAL ACTION PLAN

Once you have learned the skills and strategies for building self-esteem, tested them in practice situations, and critiqued your performance, it's for important you to develop a plan to employ the skills on a continuing basis.

Use the following chart to record and monitor your progress. If you feel you have mastered a skill, enter today's date in the first column. If you feel you would like to improve a skill, enter a check in the second column and set a date for mastering the skill in the third column. Entering all of the goal dates on the chart will help you prioritize the skills you want to learn. *Note:* Adjust your goal dates so you can concentrate on one skill at a time. After you have mastered a skill, go back to column one and enter the date it was mastered.

	Date Skill is Mastered	Want to Improve	Goal Date for Skill Mastery
Listening to and Acknowledging Thoughts and Feelings			
• Paraphrasing	_____	_____	_____
• Empathizing	_____	_____	_____
• Asking open questions	_____	_____	_____
• Asking clarifying questions	_____	_____	_____
• Responding nonverbally	_____	_____	_____
Structuring for Success			
• Setting appropriate expectations	_____	_____	_____
• Clarifying expectations	_____	_____	_____

	Date Skill is Mastered	Want to Improve	Goal Date for Skill Mastery
• Providing attractive incentives	_____	_____	_____
• Providing the appropriate amount of help	_____	_____	_____
• Removing obstacles	_____	_____	_____
• Setting appropriate standards	_____	_____	_____

Giving Students Reasonable Control

• Avoiding power struggles	_____	_____	_____
• Avoiding feelings of neglect and distrust	_____	_____	_____

Reinforcing Students as Lovable and Capable

• Offering specific encouragement and praise	_____	_____	_____
• Being specific about negative behavior	_____	_____	_____
• Separating the behavior from the person	_____	_____	_____
• Helping students avoid generalizing negative messages	_____	_____	_____
• Reinforcing effort	_____	_____	_____
• Reinforcing risk-taking	_____	_____	_____
• Reinforcing taking personal responsibility	_____	_____	_____
• Reinforcing improvement	_____	_____	_____
• Reinforcing accomplishments of which students may not be aware	_____	_____	_____
• Reinforcing feelings of being lovable	_____	_____	_____

Modeling a Positive View of Yourself

• Talking positively about yourself	_____	_____	_____
• Communicating that you can admit mistakes and rebound from them	_____	_____	_____
• Taking reasonable risks	_____	_____	_____
• Communicating that helping others benefits one's own self-esteem	_____	_____	_____
• Converting put-downs to statements of self-approval	_____	_____	_____
• Modeling persistence	_____	_____	_____
• Identifying traits/interests common to you and your students	_____	_____	_____

To follow through on your personal action plan, apply the techniques described in the Field Application sections of the workbook.

*   *   *

CONCLUSION

The principles and skills included in this workbook have proven useful to hundreds of teachers in helping students gain greater self-esteem. As a teacher, you have the opportunity and the ability to help children develop the sense of self-worth so vital to vibrant living. Best wishes as you continue your efforts to build confident, competent, lovable young people!

*   *   *

What Do I Want?

I am a teenager.
   and you ask me what I want.
I want time alone.
Alone with myself and my thoughts.
I want to be accepted for what I am
   and who I am with no strings attached.
I want to be loved by those
   who brought me into this uncertain life.
I want a house that is rich
   in honesty and sharing and caring.
I want to be heard because I just
   may have something you need to hear.
I want to know more about myself,
   my sexuality, my desires, my drives.
And I want to know God
   and to worship him in my own way.
I want to live life one step at a time
   for only then will I know its fullness.
And as I would have my life for me,
   so would I have yours for you.

— Author Unknown

Appendices

"I got two A's," the small boy said,
His voice was filled with glee.
His father very bluntly asked,
"Why didn't you get three?"

"Mom, I've got the dishes done,"
The girl called from the door.
Her mother very calmly said,
"Did you sweep the floor?"

"I mowed the grass," the tall boy said,
"And put the mower away."
His father asked him with a shrug,
"Did you clean off the clay?"

The children in the house next door
Seemed happy and content.
The same things happened over there,
But this is how it went:

"I got two A's," the small boy said,
His voice was filled with glee.
His father proudly said, "That's great;
I'm glad you belong to me."

"Mom, I've got the dishes done,"
The girl called from the door.
Her mother smiled and softly said,
"Each day I love you more."

"I mowed the grass," the tall boy said,
"And put the mower away."
His father answered with much joy,
"You've made my happy day."

Children deserve a little praise
for tasks they're asked to do.
If they're to lead a happy life,
So much depends on you.

— Author Unknown

APPENDIX A

USING THE PRINCIPLES IN THE CLASSROOM
STRUCTURING FOR SUCCESS WITH SMALL GROUPS

The following strategies are examples of ways to employ the principle of structuring for success when using small groups in the classroom.

Establishing expectations based on student ability

• Divide students into pairs when beginning small group work—students usually work best with one other student. As they adjust to group work, gradually increase the number of students in each group.

• Teach and practice essential small group skills, such as "I feel" messages and good listening skills.

• Communicate that you expect a "product" from each activity. Describe and give examples of the kind of product you expect.

Clarifying expectations

• Clearly define both the goals for the task and the goals for group operation. Give examples of how the goals in each area are to be accomplished.

• Articulate—in writing, if necessary—roles to be played by each group member. The Role Definition Sheet on page 81 illustrates how a teacher might clarify expectations for each small group member.

Providing attractive incentives

• Provide both group and individual incentives. When a group has completed a task, reward the group for both their task performance and their group process.

• Share the work of each group with the whole class.

Providing appropriate help

• Move from group to group. Show interest but resist helping unless there is a question that students cannot answer.

• Provide students with other sources of help, for example, a tutoring period at lunch run by older students or parent volunteers.

Removing obstacles

• Budget adequate time and space for tasks and projects. However, it is better to allot too little time than too much time to any one activity.

• Arrange the physical space to fit your instructional approach, whether it be small group(s), large group(s), tutoring, or role-playing.

Evaluating outcomes

• Have each group summarize the tasks they have completed and evaluate their own performance.

• Have each group evaluate the effectiveness of the group process. A simple form such as the following may help students make ratings more easily. (The "people jobs" portion of this form is based on the roles outlined in the "Role Definition Sheet" on the next page.)

People jobs	Rosa	Joe	Jenny	Leah	Tim
listens and acknowledges (acknowledger)	XXXX				
organizes group (organizer)		XX			
regulates dominance (regulator)			XXX		
reinforces others (reinforcer)				XXXX	
models self-confidence (model)					XXX
other					
Task jobs					
notes contributions					
gives directions		XXX			
reads			XXX		
summarizes	X				
other				XXX	

• Focus on behaviors, not people; emphasize positive outcomes; be specific.

There are other ways to structure small groups for success. Discuss additional methods with other teachers at your grade level, individually or in groups.

Identify other classroom activities and procedures that you use, e.g., questioning techniques, independent-study peer or cross-age tutoring, large group cooperative projects, and so on. Discuss with colleagues factors to be considered when structuring each of these activities for success.

Role Definition Sheet

Taking on the following roles will help you get the most out of your small-group learning activity. Your teacher will assign one of the roles to each member of your group. Statements are provided to help you as you carry out your role. Students and teachers who have used role definition sheets report that students feel "uplifted," "excited," and "pleasantly surprised." Although the role playing may seem contrived at first, establishing positive and clear roles for each group member is valuable and should help you feel good about yourself and your group members.

Role

Acknowledger: Listens to and acknowledges thoughts and feelings

> "Bruno, you think (say) that the author must be a conservative and is likely male, right?"
> "Jessie has a right to feel disappointed."

Organizer: Structures for success

> "Our goal today is to. . ."
> "We need to be clear about who will read next."
> "What materials [supplies] will we need to complete our project?"
> "Maria, since you know the verb forms, would you show Andrea?"

Regulator: Gives group members feelings of reasonable control

> "We need to give an opportunity to talk to those who haven't had a chance. You don't
>   have to comment, but you should know that you have the opportunity if you want it."
> "Our small group needs to become familiar with the writing style of three different
>   authors of various cultural backgrounds. Which two of the list of eight should we read
>   today and discuss tomorrow in class?"

Reinforcer: Reinforces group members as lovable and capable

> "Ahmad, you did a good job of acknowledging Jan's contribution—you were specific
>   and enthusiastic."
> "Noah, I'm glad you're in our group."

Model: Models self-confidence

> "I'm pretty good with my hands; I'll volunteer to build the model bridge."
> "I feel OK about myself—who I am—I guess I don't feel the need to prove my worth to
>   others."

*   *   *

Each of us is like an unfinished sunset.
Radiating our own special kind of light on things.
Beautiful yet always becoming.
Waiting to be appreciated.

— Jayne Trammel

APPENDIX B

BIBLIOGRAPHY

Abadzi, Helen. "Ability Grouping Effects on Academic Achievement and Self-Esteem in a Southwestern School District." *Journal of Educational Research* 77 (1984):287-92.

Anderson, E. M., G. L. Redman, and C. Rogers. *Self-Esteem for Tots to Teens*. Deephaven, MN: Meadowbrook Press, 1984; revised and expanded, Wayzata, MN: Parenting and Teaching Publications, 1991.

Atwood, M. E., and J. Williams. "Human Sexuality: An Important Aspect of Self-Image." *School Counselor* (January 1980):159-67.

Bandura, A. "Self-Efficacy: Toward a Unifying Theory of Behavioral Change." *Psychological Review* 84 (1977):191-215.

Bandura, A., N. E. Adams, and J. Beyer. "Cognitive Processes Mediating Behavioral Change." *Journal of Personality and Social Psychology* 35 (1977):125-39.

Battle, J. "Relationship Between Self-Esteem and Depression Among High School Students." *Perceptual and Motor Skills* (August, 1980).

Beane, J., and R. Lipka. *Self-Concept, Self-Esteem, and the Curriculum*. Newton, MA: Allyn & Bacon, 1984.

Bednar R., M. Wells, and S. Peterson. *Self-Esteem: Paradoxes and Innovations in Clinical Theory and Practice*. Washington DC: American Psychological Association, 1989.

Berne, P., and L. Savary. *Building Self-Esteem in Children*. Contimun, NY, 1981.

Block, J. H. *Sex Role Identity and Ego Development*. San Francisco: Jossey-Bass, 1984.

Branch, C.V., S. Damico, and W. Purkey. "A Comparison Between the Self-Concepts as Learner of Disruptive and Nondisruptive Middle School Students." *Middle School Journal* 7 (1977):15-16.

Brazelton, B., and B. Cramer. *The Earliest Relationship*. Reading, MA: Addison-Wesley, 1990.

Brockner, J. *Self-Esteem at Work: Research, Theory, and Practice*. Lexington, MA: Lexington Books/D.C. Health, 1988.

Brookover, W.B., S. Thomas, and A. Paterson. "Self-Concept of Ability and School Achievement." *Sociology of Education* 37 (1964):271-78.

Burbach, H. J., and B. Bridgeman. "Relationship Between Self-Esteem and Locus of Control in Black and White Fifth Grade Students." *Child Study Journal* 6 (1976):33-37.

Burke, J. P. "The Role of Self-Esteem in Affective Reactions to Achievement-Related Situations." *Educational and Psychological Research* 5 (1985):191-203.

Burnett, P. C. "A Self-Concept Enhancement Program for Children in the Regular Classroom." *Elementary School Guidance and Counseling* (December 1983):101-8.

Burns, R. B. *The Self-Concept*. New York: Longman, 1979.

Calsyn, R. J., and D. A. Kenny. "Self-Concept of Ability and Perceived Evaluation of Others: Cause or Effect of Academic Achievement?" *Journal of Educational Psychology* 69 (1977):136-45.

Campbell, N. K., and G. Hackett. "The Effects of Mathematics Task Performance on Math Self-Efficacy and Task Interest." *Journal of Vocational Behavior* 28 (1986):149-62.

Canfield, J., and H. C. Wells. *100 Ways to Enhance Self-Concept in the Classroom.* Englewood Cliffs, NJ: Prentice-Hall, 1976.

Coleman, J. M. "Self-Concept and the Mildly Handicapped: The Role of Social Comparisons." *Journal of Special Education* 17 (1983):37-45.

Combs, A. W., D. L. Avila, and W. W. Purkey. *Helping Relationships: Basic Concepts for the Helping Professions,* 2d ed. Boston: Allyn & Bacon, 1978.

Connell, J. P., "A Model of the Relationships Among Children's Self-related Cognitions, Affects and Academic Achievement," Unpublished doctoral dissertation, University of Denver, 1981.

Cook, J. E. "Living with What We Look Like." *Early Years* (August/September 1983):34.

Coopersmith, S. *The Antecedents of Self-Esteem.* San Francisco: W. H. Freeman, 1967.

Coopersmith, S., and R. Feldman. "Fostering a Positive Self-Concept and High Self-Esteem in the Classroom." In *Psychological Concepts in the Classroom,* edited by R. H. Coop & K. White. New York: Harper & Row, 1974.

Crane, C. "Attitudes Towards Acceptance of Self and Others and Adjustment to Teaching." *British Journal of Educational Psychology* 44 (1974):31-36.

Daly, J. A., and D. A. Wilson. "Writing Apprehension, Self-Esteem, and Personality." *Research in the Teaching of English* 17(1983):327-41.

Dobson, J. E., N. J. Campell, and R. Dobson. "The Relationships Between Children's Self-Concepts, Perceptions of School, and Life Change." *Elementary School Guidance and Counseling* (December 1982):100-107.

Dorgan, M., B. L. Goebel, and A. E. House. "Generalizing about Sex Roles and Sex-Esteem: Results or Effects?" *Sex Roles* 9(1983):719-23.

Dreikurs, R. *Psychology in the Classroom.* New York: Harper & Row, 1968.

Durbin, D. M. "Multimodel Group Sessions to Enhance Self-Concept." *Elementary School Guidance and Counseling* (April 1982):288-95.

Elkind, D. *A Sympathetic Understanding of the Child: Birth to Sixteen.* Boston: Allyn & Bacon, 1971.

Ellis, A., and R. Harper. *A New Guide to Rational Living.* North Hollywood, CA: Wilshire, 1975.

Erickson, E. H. *Identity, Youth, and Crisis.* New York: W. W. Norton, 1968.

Falcione, R. L., L. Sussman, and R. P. Herden. "Communication Climate in Organizations." In *Handbook of Organizational Communication,* edited by F. M. Jablin et al., 195-227. Newbury Park: Sage Publications, 1987.

Frey, D., and C. J. Carlock. *Enhancing Self-Esteem.* Muncie, IN: Accelerated Development Publishers, 1989.

Gibson, S., and M. Dembo. "Teacher Efficacy: A Construct Validation." *Journal of Educational Psychology* 76(1984):569-82.

Gilligan, C. *In a Different Voice.* Cambridge, MA: Harvard University Press, 1982.

Ginott, H. G. *Teacher and Child.* New York: Macmillan, 1972.

Good, T. L., B. J. Biddle, and J. E. Brophy. *Teachers Make a Difference.* New York: Holt, Rinehart & Winston, 1975.

Gorrell, J., and E. W. Capron. "Effects of Instructional Type and Feedback on Prospective Teachers' Self-Efficacy Beliefs." *Journal of Experimental Education* 56 (1988):120-3.

Gottsdanker-Willekens, A. E., and P. Y. Leonard. "All About Me: Language Arts Strategies to Enhance Self-Concept." *Classroom Reading Teacher* (April 1984):801-02.

Gunderson, B., and D. W. Johnson. "Building Positive Attitudes by Using Cooperative Learning Groups." *Foreign Language Annals* 13 (1980):39-46.

Hall, H., and K. Runion. "Are Teachers Effective in Self-Concept Development?" *College Student Journal* 17 (1983):61-64.

Hall, H., C. Vernon, and D. Kaye. *The Development of the Self-Concept During the Adolescent Years.* Chicago: University of Chicago Press, 1981.

Hansforth, B. C., and J. A. Hattie. "The Relationship Between Self and Achievement/Performance Measures." *Review of Educational Research* 52 (1982):123-42.

Harter, S. *Manual for the Self-Perception Profile for Children.* University of Denver, 1985.

Held, L. "Self-Esteem and Social Network of the Young Pregnant Teenager." *Adolescence,* v. XVI, no. 64, Winter 1981.

Holte, C. S., et al. "Influence of Children's Positive Self-Perceptions on Donating Behavior in a Naturalistic Setting." *Journal of School Psychology* 22 (1984):145-53.

Hong, S. M. "Self-Concepts of Korean High School Students as Related to Socio-Economic Status." *Psychological Reports* 50 (1982):15-18.

Horney, K. "The Search for Glory." in *Social Psychology of the Self-Concept,* edited by M. Rosenberg and H. B. Kaplan, 102-7. Arlington Heights, IL: Harlan Davidson, 1982.

Hummel, R., and L. L. Roselli. "Identity Status and Academic Achievement in Female Adolescents." *Adolescence* 18 (1983):17-27.

Jensen, M. A. "Self-Concept and Its Relation to Age, Family Structure, and Gender in Head Start Children." *Journal of Psychology* 113 (1983):89-94.

Johnson, R., and D. W. Johnson. "Building Friendships Between Handicapped and Nonhandicapped Students: Effects of Cooperative and Individualized Instruction." *American Educational Research Journal* 18 (1981):415-24.

Johnson, R., et al. "Integrating Severely Adaptively Handicapped Seventh-Grade Students into Constructive Relationships with Nonhandicapped Peers in Science Class." *American Journal of Mental Deficiency* 87 (1983):611-18.

Kostelnik, M. *Guiding Children's Social Development.* Cincinnati, OH: Southwestern Publishing, 1988.

Kugle, C. L., R. O. Clements, and P. M. Powell. "Level and Stability of Self-Esteem in Relation to Academic Behavior of Second Graders." *Journal of Personality and Social Psychology* 44 (1983):201-7.

LaMascus, V. "You Can If You Think You Can: Using Affirmations to Build Your Students' Self-Confidence." *Perspectives for Teachers of the Hearing Impaired* 4 (1985):2-4.

Lay, R., and J. Wakstein. "Race, Academic Achievement, and Self-Concept of Ability." *Research in Higher Education* 22 (1985):43-64.

Lent, R. W., S. D. Brown, and K. C. Larkin. "Relation of Self-Efficacy Expectations to Academic Achievement and Persistence." *Journal of Counseling Psychology* 31 (1984):356-62.

Lerner, B. "Self-Esteem and Excellence: The Choice and the Paradox." *American Educator* 9 (1985):10-16.

Lickona, T. *Raising Good Children.* New York: Bantam Books, 1983.

Maddux, J. E., L. W. Norton, and C. D. Stoltenberg. "Self-Efficacy Expectancy, Outcome Expectancy, and Outcome Value: Relative Effects on Behavioral Intentions." *Journal of Personality and Social Psychology* 51 (1986):783-89.

Marsh, H. W., and J. W. Parker. "Determinants of Student Self-Concept: Is It Better to Be a Relatively Large Fish in a Small Pond Even if You Don't Learn to Swim as Well?" *Journal of Personality and Social Psychology* 47 (1984):213-31.

Marsh, H. W., and R. Shavelson. "Self-Concept: Its Multifaceted, Hierarchical Structure." *Educational Psychologist* 20 (1985):107-23.

Marsh, H. W., I. D. Smith, and J. Barnes. "Multidimensional Self-Concepts: Relation With Sex and Academic Achievement." *Journal of Educational Psychology* 77:581-596.

Marsh, H. W., I. D. Smith, and J. Barnes. "Multitrait-Multimethod Analyses of the Self-Description Questionnaire: Student-Teacher Agreement on Multidimensional Ratings of Student Self-Concept." *American Educational Research Journal* 20 (1983):333-57.

McAuley, E. "Modeling and Self-Efficacy: A Test of Bandura's Model." *Journal of Sport Psychology* 7 (1985):283-95.

McKay, M., and P. Fanning. *Self-Esteem.* Oakland, CA: New Harbinger Publications, 1987.

Mendelson, B. K., and D. R. White. "Development of Self-Body-Esteem in Overweight Youngsters." *Developmental Psychology* 21 (1985):90-96.

Norem-Hebeisen, A., and D. W. Johnson. "Relationships Between Cooperative, Competitive, and Individualistic Attitudes and Differentiated Aspects of Self-Esteem." *Journal of Personality* 49 (1981):415-25.

Norwich, B. "A Case-Study Investigating the Relationship Between Perceived Self-Efficacy and Performance at Subtraction Tasks." *Educational Psychology* 5 (1985):45-53.

Nucci, L. "Knowledge of the Learner: The Development of Children's Concepts of Self, Morality and Societal Convention" in Reynolds, M. *Knowledge Base for the Beginning Teacher.* New York: Pergamon Press for AACTE, 1989.

Patten, M. D. "Relationships Between Self-Esteem, Anxiety, and Achievement in Young Learning Disabled Students." *Journal of Learning Disabilities* 16 (1983):43-45.

Phillips, R. H. "Increasing Positive Self-Referent Statements to Improve Self-Esteem in Low-Income Elementary School Children." *Journal of Educational Psychology* 22 (1984):155-63.

Post-Kammer, P., and P. L. Smith. "Sex Differences in Career Self-Efficacy, Consideration, and Interests of Eighth and Ninth Graders." *Journal of Counseling Psychology* 29 (1985):551-59.

Purkey, W. *Self-Concept and School Achievement.* Englewood Cliffs, NJ: Prentice-Hall, 1970.

Purkey, W., and N. Novak. *Inviting School Success: A Self-Concept Approach to Teaching and Learning,* 2d ed. Englewood Cliffs, NJ: Prentice-Hall, 1984.

Purkey, W., A. Raheim, and B. Cage. "Self-Concept as Learner: An Overlooked Part of Self-Concept Theory." *Humanistic Education and Development* 22 (1983):52-57.

Quandt, I., and R. Selznick. *Self-Concept and Reading.* Newark, NJ: International Reading Association, 1984.

Reasoner, R. W., *Building Self-Esteem: Teachers' Guide and Classroom Materials.* Palo Alto, CA: Consulting Psychologists Press, 1982.

Redman, G. L. "A Model for Human Relations Inservice Training." *Journal of Teacher Education* 28 (1977):34-38.

-------------. "A Study of Effects of Staff Development Program on Building Self-Esteem and on Levels of Self-Esteem of Pupils," Unpublished report, Hamline University, St. Paul, MN, 1991.

-------------. "Building Self-Esteem in Children: Practical Principles and Skills." Monograph. *Early Childhood Resources in Education* In ERIC, 1987.

-------------. *Building Self-Esteem in Children: A Skill and Strategy Workbook for Parents.* Wayzata MN: Parenting and Teaching Publications, 1986, revised and expanded 1992.

-------------. *Building Self-Esteem in Students: A Skill and Strategy Workbook for Teachers.* Wayzata MN: Parenting and Teaching Publications, 1986, revised and expanded 1992.

-------------. "Effects of Value Clarification Training on Student Self-Concept." *Journal of Teaching and Learning* 4 (1978):28-36.

Reed, R. *Talking With Children.* Denver, CO: Arden Press, 1983.

Rosenberg, M., and L. I. Pearlin. "Social Class and Self-Esteem among Children and Adults." In *Social Psychology of the Self-Concept,* edited by M. Rosenberg and H. B. Kaplan, 268-88. Arlington Heights, IL: Harlan Davidson, 1982.

Rosenberg, M., and H. B. Kaplan, eds. *Social Psychology of the Self-Concept.* Arlington Heights, IL: Harlan Davidson, 1982.

Samuels, S. C. *Enhancing Self-Concept in Early Childhood.* New York: Human Science Press, 1977.

Schunk, D. H. "Effects of Effort Attributional Feedback on Children's Perceived Self-Efficacy and Achievement." *Journal of Educational Psychology* 74 (1982a):548-56.

-------------. "Participation in Goal Setting: Effects on Self-Efficacy and Skills of Learning-Disabled Children." *Journal of Special Education* 19 (1985):307-17.

------------. "Progress Self-Monitoring Effects on Children's Self-Efficacy and Achievement." *Journal of Experimental Education* 51 (1982b):89-93.

------------. "Verbalization and Children's Self-Regulated Learning." *Contemporary Educational Psychology* 11 (1986):347-69.

Schunk, D. H., and T. P. Gunn. "Modeled Importance of Task Strategies and Achievement Beliefs: Effect on Self-Efficacy and Skill Development." *Journal of Early Adolescence* 5 (1985):247-58.

Schunk, D. H., and A. R. Hanson. "Peer Models: Influence on Children's Self-Efficacy and Achievement." *Journal of Educational Psychology* 77 (1985):313-22.

Schunk, D. H., A. R. Hanson, and P. D. Cox. "Peer Model Attributes and Children's Achievement Behaviors." *Journal of Educational Psychology* 79 (1987):54-61.

Shavelson, R. J., and R. Bolus. "Self-Concept: The Interplay of Theory and Methods." *Journal of Educational Psychology* 74 (1982):3-17.

Silvernail, David. *Developing Positive Student Self-Concept*. Washington, D.C.: National Education Association, 1981.

Simon, S. B., L. W. Howe, and H. Kirschenbaum. *Values Clarification: A Handbook of Practical Strategies for Teachers and Students*. New York: Hart, 1972.

Snyder, M. *Public Appearances/Private Realities: The Psychology of Self-Monitoring*. New York: W. H. Freeman, 1987.

Snygg, D., and A. W. Combs. *Individual Behavior: A New Frame of Reference for Psychology*. New York: Harper, 1949.

Spitz, R. A. "Hospitalism: An Inquiry into the Genesis of Psychiatric Conditioning in Early Childhood." In *The Psychoanalytic Study of the Child*, edited by R. S. Eissler et al, vol. 1. New York: International Universities Press, 1945.

Stake, J. E. "The Ability/Performance Dimension of Self-Esteem: Implications for Women's Achievement Behavior." *Psychology of Women Quarterly* 3 (1979):365-77.

Tierno, M. J. "Responding to Self-Concept Disturbances among Early Adolescents: A Psychosocial View for Educators." *Adolescence* 18 (1983):577-84.

Tunney, Jim. "Self-Esteem and Participation—Two Basics for Student Achievement." *National Association of Secondary School Principals Bulletin* 68 (1984):117-21.

Wagner, J. W. L. "Self Concept: Research and Educational Implications." *Studies in Educational Evaluation* 9 (1983):239-51.

Weinhold, B. K., and J. Hilferty. "The Self-Esteem Matrix Tool for Elementary Counselors." *Elementary School Guidance and Counseling* (April 1983):243-51.

White, B., B. T. Kaban, and J. S. Attanucci. *The Origins of Human Competence: Final Report of the Harvard Pre-School Project*. Lexington, MA: Lexington Press, 1979.

Wylie, R. *Theory and Research on Selected Topics*. Vol. 2 of *The Self-Concept*. Lincoln: University of Nebraska Press, 1979.

Yamamoto, K. *The Child and His Image: Self-Concept in the Early Years*. Boston: Houghton-Mifflin, 1972.

Zimmerman, B. J., and J. Ringle. "Effects of Model Persistence and Statements of Confidence on Children's Self-Efficacy and Problem Solving." *Journal of Educational Psychology* 73 (1981):485-93.

*   *   *

Probably the most important requirement for effective behavior, central to the whole problem, is self-esteem.

— Stanley Coopersmith

APPENDIX C

MATERIALS FOR INDIVIDUALS AND FOR INSTRUCTORS OF WORKSHOPS AND COURSES

■ Anderson, E. M., G. L. Redman, and C. Rogers. *Self-Esteem for Tots to Teens.* Parenting and Teaching Publications, Inc., 1984, revised 1991. ($7.95)

Without jargon or complicated theory, the authors show busy teachers, parents, and others who work with children how to apply five easy-to-learn principles for building self-esteem in children. Each chapter describes one of the principles and provides many real-life vignettes illustrating how to apply the principle to children at different stages of development. The book is a useful addition to home, school, and public libraries; as a text in seminars, workshops, and courses for adults; and as a text for secondary classes that offer units on self-esteem, e.g., health, home economics, and psychology classes. (Volume discount available.)

About the Authors

Eugene Anderson, Ed.D., is a professor of education at the University of Minnesota. George Redman, Ph.D., is a professor of education at Hamline University in St. Paul. Charlotte Rogers, Ph.D., is a developmental psychologist for the Minneapolis Public Schools.

About the Book

"I wish every parent, day-care provider, and teacher would read this book and practice its principles."

> Dr. Norman Sprinthall
> Coauthor of *Adolescent Psychology:*
> *A Developmental View.*

"I am very impressed with its content and style. A . . . beautifully written book with such profound importance for parents and teachers."

> Dr. Maryann J. Ehle
> Professor of Education
> West Liberty State College

"The principles are most important. Your sensitivity is a strength throughout the book."

> Dr. William Purkey
> Author of *Self-Concept and School Achievement* and coauthor of *Inviting School Success*

■ Redman, G. L. *Building Self-Esteem in Students: A Skill and Strategy Workbook for Teachers*, Parenting and Teaching Publications, Inc., 1986, revised 1992. ($19.95)

Based on the five principles for building self-esteem as described in *Self-Esteem for Tots to Teens*, this workbook helps teachers—preschool, K-12, and post secondary—to learn and practice in a guided setting the skills and strategies for building self-esteem in students.

The workbook will help you to

• Learn the critical elements of each skill
• Recognize examples of the skill
• Practice, in writing, how to perform the skill
• Work effectively with colleagues in learning and using the skills

As a complement to *Self-Esteem for Tots to Teens*, this "learn-by-doing" workbook has proven useful to individual teachers as well as to groups of teachers in staff development workshops and continuing education classes. Guidelines are provided for learning and practicing the skills in small groups.

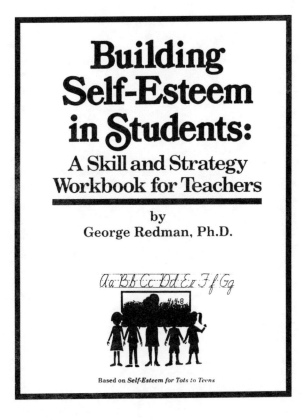

About the Workbook

"The workbook is clearly written and easy to understand. The learn-through-practice approach is a fun and effective way to learn skills for building self-esteem. The ideas in the workbook motivate teachers to expand on vistas important to children and youth of all ethnic and cultural backgrounds."

S. J. Hernandez
Specialist on cultural diversity
and public school teacher

Comments by Teachers Who Have Completed Workshops and Classes

"I found the workbook to be very clear. I could, at my own pace, complete each section and internalize each skill described."

"Several of us discussed the exercises outside of our continuing education class. It was fun and gave me a broader perspective on how and when to use the skills."

"I liked the workbook. It made me think about how I was using the skills and how I will use them in the future."

■ Redman, G. L. *Building Self-Esteem in Children: A Skill and Strategy Workbook for Parents.* Parenting and Teaching Publications, Inc. 1986, revised 1992. ($19.95)

This version of the workbook, geared for parents rather than teachers, has been enthusiastically received by parents, parent educators, and others who care for children. It has been used in community education parenting programs, in parent libraries and is endorsed by personnel in mental health and drug abuse prevention programs as well as other organizations that work with youth.

The workbook will help you to

• Learn the critical elements of each skill
• Recognize the examples of the skill
• Practice, in writing, how to perform the skill
• Work effectively with colleagues in learning and using the skills

A "learn-by-doing" workbook that complements **Self-Esteem for Tots to Teens.**

Building Self-Esteem in Children: A Skill and Strategy Workbook for Parents

by
George Redman, Ph.D.

Based on *Self-Esteem for Tots to Teens*

About the Workbook:

"I was impressed with the material contained within this workbook. It will be useful in our work with children as a resource for family members."

Dr. B. Garfinkel, M.D., F.R.C.P. (C)
Director, Child and Adolescent Psychiatry
University of Minnesota

"As a single parent, I recognize the importance of both quality time and the quantity of time a parent spends with a child. This workbook has helped me make the most of the time I spend with Kerstin and Justin."

Jim Merritt, parent
River Falls, Wisconsin

*   *   *

Order Form

Qty.	Title	Order No.	Unit Cost	Total
	Self-Esteem for Tots to Teens By E. Anderson, G. Redman, and C. Rogers	100	7.95	
	Building Self-Esteem in Children: A Skill and Strategy Workbook for Parents By G. Redman	110	19.95	
	Building Self-Esteem in Students: A Skill and Strategy Workbook for Teachers By G. Redman	120	19.95	
			Subtotal	
			MN residents add 6% sales tax	
			Shipping and Handling (see below)	
			Total	

Shipping and Handling
Book: Add $1.25 for postage and handling for first book and $.50 for each additional book.
Workbook: Add $2.00 for postage and handling for first workbook and $.75 for each additional workbook.
Canada and Overseas: Add $2.00 to the above shipping and handling charges for books shipped to Canada. Overseas postage will be billed.
Quantity discounts: For orders including six or more items, a 10% discount is available.

Send book(s) to:
Name _____
Address _____
City _____ State _____ ZIP _____

Make check or money order payable to:
Parenting and Teaching Publications, 16686 Meadowbrook Lane, Wayzata, MN 55391.
Phone orders: (612) 473-1793

Thank you for purchasing one of our products. We take great pride in publishing high quality materials.

We are interested in knowing about our customers. Could you please answer the following for us:

How did you first hear about our products? _____

_____

Where did you buy your book/workbook(s)? _____

_____

Occupation: _____

Comments: _____

_____

_____

May we use your comments in our promotional materials?

Yes   No   (circle) _____
                                              (signature)

If there is someone who you think might be interested in receiving information about our products, please let us know their address. We will be happy to send a brochure.

Name _____

Address _____

City _____

State/Zipcode _____